How to write a how to write book

Brian Piddock

A few reviews of **How to write a how to write book** *by some of the many satisfied customers:*

Thank you for everything, Brian. My *"How to Write a Glossy Gardening Manual with Full Colour Photos"* has been snapped up by the publishers!
Jeff Kerm, Adelaide

I took your advice and after years of failure can now sit back and watch the cheques come in for my *"How To Write a Thriller about a Deadly Terror Attack in a Western City"*.
Alice Bowen, Grimsby

Brian, you saved my life! I was getting nowhere till I followed your book, and now my *"How To Write a Diet Doctors' Detox Manual"* is in the bestsellers' charts!
John Dickson, San Francisco

Entirely unsolicited comments freely sent in by appreciative readers.

About the Author

A uthor Brian Piddock is our foremost How To Write writer. Self-effacing to a fault, he insists he would rather not have any biographical information printed about himself. "I'm not secretive," he says, "but I deplore the present trend of the celebrity. My work reveals all that anyone needs to know about my life."

How to write a how to write book

Brian Piddock

NEIL RHODES BOOKS

Published by Neil Rhodes Books
Well Cottage
Wern
Llanymynech
SY22 6PF
email: nr@neilrhodes.co.uk

www.neilrhodesbooks.com
www.brianpiddock.co.uk

Illustrations by Anthony Connolly
Cover design by Elspeth Edmondson

British Library Cataloguing in Publication Data
A catalogue record for this book is available from the British Library

ISBN 978-0-9555557-0-1

Printed and bound in Great Britain by
Antony Rowe Ltd, Chippenham and Eastbourne

Contents

Acknowledgments   vii
Introduction   ix

1

Why do you want to be a how to write writer?   1

2

Write what you know   7

3

Choosing your subject   15

4

Categories   25

5

Categories (2) (category 2)   33

6

Study the genre   45

7

Research   49

8

Structure   57

9

Style   65

10

Technique   73

11

The title   81

12

Your day   95

13

Writer's block   103

14
Your audience   111
15
Presentation   121
16
Submitting your idea   131
17
Publishers and agents   139
18
The world wide web   143
19
Self-publishing   149
20
Unusual ways of publishing   159
21
Redrafting   167
22
Payment   171
23
Translations   177
24
Bursaries and grants   183
25
Awards and festivals   191
26
Writers' courses   197
27
Conclusion   201
28
FAQs   209
29
Epilogue   217
Appendixes   219
Index   223

Acknowledgments

Thanks must go to all the people without whom not getting up in the morning would be less worthwhile:

My family, of course, for their constant help and support.

Miss Simms, for the early encouragement that set me on this long and fulfilling road.

Diane, for all those fond memories that still sustain me in my darkest hours.

Abbie, whom I forgive, because to forgive is divine.

But especially to Ryan and Laura, because without them I wouldn't be where I am today.

Oh, and not forgetting young Anthony Connolly, who's done a few illustrations. Neil Rhodes is someone from college I hadn't seen for ages until I bumped into him at our old mate Jim's funeral recently, and he happened to mention he was in publishing, and I happened to mention I'd got this book, and one thing led to another, and — call me sentimental if you want — that's why I chose the present publisher above all the others to publish this book.

Neil did say he had a brother-in-law who was a bit of an artist, and I'm happy to give a lad a helping hand, especially since he seemed personable enough, despite the nose piercing and gelled spiky hair.

So Anthony will be helping to clarify any of the more difficult instructions I have to give. I don't anticipate too many of those, luckily! I've been in this game long enough to know how to explain through words and not to need pictures, thank goodness.

Author Brian Piddock

This is supposed to be me, done by Anthony Connolly.

I actually met young Anthony, at publisher Neil Rhodes's office. He dashed in, mobile to his ear, grunted a couple of words, nodded at me when we were introduced, and dashed out before I could ask him how school was, his mobile still attached to his ear. He ought to get surgery for that.

I don't suppose that was how Rembrandt used to get his subjects to pose, but then I don't suppose Rembrandt was in a hurry all the time to get from one club to the next, like young Anthony. Still, I do admire the way the artists like him (Anthony, not Rembrandt) can capture someone with just a few lines of a pencil. Even if I'm not at all bald like this, slightly receding is the very most even my worst enemies would say, and I've never had a cane, and I don't have a suit. Not any more. At least not one I can get hold of.

But perhaps this is how young Anthony imagines I will look like, in a couple of decades, when I'm considered the Grand Man of belle lettres. Especially belles comment écrire lettres.

Actually, I suppose that's Anthony's way of giving a compliment. So thank you, young Anthony.

Introduction

I love writing.

I've always loved it. Every second of every day of my life.

Except, I suppose, if you're going to be picky, the time that you may have read about in the worst and most libellous and uncaring tabloid newspapers. The time when I was in that house and the room was a blazing inferno of manuscripts and paper, and the police were hammering at the door, and I had almost been killed by a thug who later got off scot-free while I was persecuted and prosecuted even though I was entirely the victim of that horrendous crime.

Perhaps apart from that moment.

And this book certainly isn't the place to tell that story, fascinating though it is.

Yes, I can certainly say, apart from that brief time from which I was lucky to escape with my life and for which I still haven't received proper justice even though I've tried everything I can, I have always loved writing.

I remember when I was 7, and I wrote my first short story: **Fruggles the Friendly Hedgehog**. I remember even then the hard work I put in to make sure that every word was the right word. And how my teacher, Miss Simms, a lovely kind lady with glasses and grey hair, gave me a tick and said:

"Well done, Brian."

Especially since in her ferocious moments she was someone who could make us wet ourselves if we even thought about being naughty.

That moment of praise has stayed with me throughout my

life. It's what we all want to hear, when our literary efforts are read.

"Well done, Brian."

Or whatever your name happens to be.

Fruggles the Friendly Hedgehog *

* *Ha ha! What an amusing lad that young Anthony Connolly is.*
All I can say is it's a good job he's publisher Neil Rhodes's brother-in-law, or I might be a little offended that he's chosen to take the mickey out of the cherished memory I have of that story I wrote — my first story, and one written with all the delicate innocence only a child has. Still, I can take a joke. Just don't make too many more like that, young Anthony!

That may well have been the moment I decided to become a writer.

The moment I realised:

I love writing.

Even now, after a long career in the business, I find nothing more satisfying than waking up on a lovely summer morning, having a fresh croissant and an espresso, getting down to my study, switching on the computer, and contentedly tapping away as the word count ticks over.

Or, if not study, shed down the bottom of the garden. Or room, if that's all you've got. It's all I've got, these days, thanks to that major miscarriage of justice I mentioned above. But a room is all I need.

And it's not just the words you must love.

It's the ideas. The planning. The structure. And then seeing your words and ideas in print.

A book. With your name on it. That's what you must love.

That's why I love writing. And of all the writing I love, the writing I love best is the writing of:

How To Write Books.

I hope you know you can love it too, because I don't think you should consider being a How To Write writer unless you know you can love writing How To Write Books almost as much as I do. I say 'almost' because you'll never be able to love it as much as I do. That isn't possible.

Let me make one thing clear: I can't teach you everything. But I am one of the privileged few to have the experience to teach you almost everything you need to know, and that's more than all the research or reading in the world can do.

But you must love your work.

I do.

Wherever I am, the study in that beautiful house in quiet suburbia, or here, with the traffic and the net curtains and the dark and inadequate furniture, I love writing How To Write Books.

It's my joy. It's my bliss. It's my life.

Follow me, then, and in a few simple steps that anyone who knows they can love writing How To Write Books will be able to follow, I will make it your joy, your bliss, and your life.

chapter one

Why do you want to be a how to write writer?

First, obviously, because like me you love writing, and especially you love writing How To Write Books. It's your joy, your bliss, your life (see *Introduction*).

Second, you've probably written something already. I hope you have. I wouldn't recommend telling other people how to write when you haven't tried it yourself! Not that that stops some people doing exactly that. Down the pub, for example, you're always guaranteed to meet some friends with their advice, especially when you tell them what you're working on.

"I don't see who'd want to read anything like that," someone will say.

Or:

"That isn't very interesting."

Or even:

"What a bloody stupid idea!"

It could easily drive a less centred person than myself into an absolute blind fury and want to rip their insides out with my bare hands and then shove a pint glass into their stomachs, except of course the reason I love going down the pub is for the chat, the bonhomie, and the freely given and accepted comments.

So you've written a short story, or even a novel, or autobiography, or history. You may have managed to interest a publisher. They seemed quite keen. You had that wonderful experience of imagining holding in your hand a volume on which appears your name. You'll never forget that moment. I remember when I wrote my first book (**The Dark Interloper**), typed up on an old manual typewriter — because we didn't have personal computers back in 1979 — and I bound it together, and put on a carefully hand drawn cover, and I held the manuscript that seemed to me perfect in every way. What an unforgettable moment.

__The Dark Interloper__, by **Brian Piddock**. 42 pages. 1979.

Unforgettable.

But perhaps, like mine, your work didn't quite get into print. Publishers were interested, yes, but suggested it might be a little 'skimpy', despite your pointing out that the great classic French novel *L'Etranger* by Albert Camus is only 38000 words long. And being 17, with the inflexibility of youth, you refused to change a word, or add any extraneous matter to beef it up to a length certain unperceptive publishers considered 'acceptable'.

FACT BOX 1

I haven't looked at **The Dark Interloper** for a very long time, but would be surprised if it didn't still have the power to shock and delight in equal measure. It tells the story of a sensitive and creative boy (all right, I admit it, a trifle autobiographical!) being bullied at school by his unfeeling peers, until a stranger comes along and deals with the bullies. Though there is a considerable amount of graphic violence in the book, because it is dealt with in such an imaginative way it could not possibly offend anyone. In fact, I believe it would warm most hearts, especially since it ends in a complete triumph for the hero and his friend, and the bullies get mangled and/or dead!

You came very close, and that's not bad for a first work at that age, especially considering the London Literary Mafia that only publishes its own certified back-scratching members. Because after all the London Literary Mafia doesn't want anyone breaking into their little world, where every other novel features some deadbeat writer having a banal marital affair with some other writer in an Islington kitchen.

Why are there so many novels about writers? Because that's all that London Literary Mafia writers know. They've got such a limited horizon. No real person wants to know about the lives of London Literary Mafia writers, but nothing else ever gets published so we don't have any choice in the matter.

Let's say, for example, you got 38 rejection letters, ranging from the kind to the uninterested. Perhaps you put **The Dark Interloper** aside, an ambitious work that will be published to considerable acclaim once you're famous and in the position of instructing publishers exactly what constitutes an acceptable length for a novel.

Instead, undaunted, because this is only the first step on your long journey to literary superstardom, you write your second work:

The Walking Wounded by **Brian Piddock**. 562 pages. 1982.

This time you are absolutely confident of success, such is the power of the writing and the relevance of the subject matter. But those same publishers who said they would love to see

---

FACT BOX 2

No one could accuse **The Walking Wounded** of being skimpy. It's a fully comprehensive view of Britain in the early 1980s, when being a supporter of the Thatcher government at a provincial university was extremely unpopular. I know.

Not that the hero, a young man of considerable literary faculties, is at all daunted by notions of mere popularity, such are his strong moral principles. And as it happens, he's very popular with many beautiful and intelligent girls!

---

anything else you've done, feel it's not quite up to the standard of the first, and in today's economic climate, etc etc, when what they mean is they don't intend to take any risks, even if with a little investment and a little encouragement you would win them the Man Booker Prize within five years.

So you turn to the world of live drama and adapt your novel for the stage, with a slightly simplified story. And you find the theatre is even more of a closed shop than the publishing industry! In fact 28 of the 30 theatres you send **The Wounded Walk** to don't even bother to return the script, and the other two have obviously used it for mopping up coffee spillages.

But you get some of the students at your university to put it on, and it goes down very well, even if the director hasn't quite grasped the sexual tension that's meant to be there, the actors fluff so many lines the prompt takes a curtain call, and you get blamed for being repetitive because the performers can't appreciate the poetic rhythm of your dialogue.

The first night of 'The Wounded Walk'.
And the last night of 'The Wounded Walk' *

So you try radio, but since you're not gay, disabled, or black, the BBC doesn't want to know about **The Walk of the Wounded**.

---

* *Very droll, young Anthony, but in fact we had a very large and enthusiastic audience. Fairly, anyway. For a while. Well, it's not the writer's fault if the acting isn't up to the standard of the dialogue, is it? Nor if the audience have got mosquito-sized attention spans.*

But you love writing. The clack of the keys. The words on the screen. The flowing sentences. You're not going to give up. It's your life. It's what you were put on this earth to do. It would be a crime against nature if you considered for one moment abandoning writing.

Luckily, you don't need to. There is a direction left for you to take. You turn to the one genre that will always sell, and doesn't require a celebrity name on the dust jacket or for you to be best mates with Martin Amis.

It is, of course:

How To Write Books.

FACT BOX 3

Some How To Write writers use the TLAs 'HTWB' and 'HTWW', to, they claim, save space and simplify things. I think it's just laziness, and leads to confusion.
(In case you're not au fait with the literary and typographical terminology, TLA stands for Three Letter Acronym, HTWB for How To Write Books, and HTWW for How To Write Writer).

Let me recap:

You have something to say.

You want to say it.

You need to say it.

It's your life, your joy, your bliss.

But no one will listen.

So you help other people to say what they want to say, and you have achieved your ambition of seeing your words in print. If those other people are, unfortunately, as unsuccessful as you were, and they too enter that blackness of depression that is known only to those whose literary efforts are unappreciated or, even worse, unread, and they roam the streets cursing the human race for its blindness and ignorance, then at least you have the satisfaction known to all teachers at all times, that they couldn't have done it without you.

But let us be quite clear, right from the start.

Let me get the warning on the packet out of the way.

Not "Smoking Kills". Or even "Writing Kills". It doesn't. Well, it can, it almost killed me, but that's another story, and this book certainly isn't the place to tell that story, even though it's begging to be told, and told truthfully for once.

But: *"It's A Tough Business"*.

FACT BOX 4

Actually, I suppose HTWB and HTWW are FLAs, or Four Letter Acronyms (which is itself, funnily enough, a TLA, or Three Letter Acronym).

You'll find you have a lot of rivals. You may know them. In this average sized town I ended up in, I know at least one other HTWW (TLA for How To Write Writer — see *Fact Box 3*). I've met, in committees and groups around the country, a few more. They may not be as talented as me. They may happen to be luckier, and they may happen to know the right people. Life isn't fair, and it's at its most unfair in the literary world which is our playground and battlefield.

But you, like me, will rise above the injustice of this cruel world. Why? I've already told you. Do I need to remind you already? As Miss Simms would have said: *"Concentrate*, Brian!" (or whatever your name happens to be).

It's because you love writing, and especially you love writing How To Write Books.

You haven't been as successful as you deserve to be. You haven't been at all successful. That's a shame, but it's no reason to join the army and get yourself killed in some foreign land. No, you are precisely the kind of person the world of How To Write Books welcomes and needs.

Welcome!

chapter two

Write what you know

I n every How To Write Book that has ever existed or ever will exist, you will always find one piece of advice, which is the First Rule of How To Write Books:

RULE 1
Write what you know.

And there it is, in this book, so no one can say this How To Write Book breaks the first rule of How To Write Books. And it's the First Rule of How To Write Books for a very good reason.

Because it's true!

FACT BOX 5

T hat first rule of writing. I know what you're thinking. You're young and idealistic. We all were, once. You're saying, "I don't believe in rules, man. I'm free. I'm an artist." You're quite entitled to think that. But trust me. You'll come round, sooner or later, and it would save everyone a lot of time and trouble if it was sooner. No one likes a clever dick.

Let me illustrate this fact by getting you to imagine something, a thought experiment, if you will.

You're a binman.

Well, of course that's not your proper job, you're just doing it to earn some money. People who are binmen full-time and permanently can hardly string a sentence together, let alone write it down.

That was my experience, and it wasn't pleasant, those six weeks in 1984, but I was desperate, and hungry, and more particularly thirsty, because there's nothing wrong with going to the pub, a source of a million stories is the pub, and there's nothing worse than sitting on your own at 9.30 in the evening in your room with not enough money in your pocket for a pint and no one you don't owe money to likely to be in the pub to offer you a drink.

This was, of course, before I gave all that up to settle down and become blissfully married and have two lovely darling children.

So, to prevent the Social Security stopping your piffling few quid and your rent, you accept the only job in the job centre.

A binman.

The trouble is, it's hell.

You get rotting vegetables dropping on your head. You get maggots in your hair. You get called a student by your ignorant fellow workers even though you left college three months ago. If there's a butt for a joke you are it. And they're not even vaguely amusing jokes. Being told you've got to go to the works department and collect a bucket of steam. That wouldn't make a child laugh, and no, I didn't fall for it, I was just going along with their pathetic attempt at humour.

And it would take a rather stupid sadist to find putting someone upside-down in a wheely bin amusing. It's not amusing, I can tell you. You can hurt your neck quite badly, it's smelly, and if you're at all prone to claustrophobia, like me, it's a truly terrifying experience, and ought to have led to their dismissal, if the supervisor had had any sense of justice and wasn't their mate.

At the end of the day you shower, you scrub yourself with soap, you have hour-long baths, you cover your body in deodorant, and still throughout the night the only odour in your nose is putrefaction.

It's the worst six weeks of your life, alleviated only by one piece of good fortune, when a bin is dropped on your toe and you're safely invalided out of the job.

No, it wasn't hell. It made hell look like Kew Gardens. Being tortured with red hot irons would have been a relief.

The bins of Burnley *

But there is something you can get out of the whole ghastly experience.

You now know what it is to be a binman. These people are your people. You have lived their life. You can feel true empathy for them. The next Christmas they knock on your door for their tip you won't slam the door in their face. No, you'll tell them they've got an incredible nerve asking for a tip when they earn about twenty times more than you do, and then slam the

---

*Well done, young Anthony, you've managed to capture all the pain and unpleasantness of that job I had, one that scarred me for so long. Though I have to say the bins weren't in Burnley. They weren't anywhere near Burnley. They were in a town so hated I cannot even mention its name. It did begin with a B, though, by an interesting coincidence.

door in their face.

You are one of them. This is a world you now know about. You have a subject for a work of fiction.

Especially since, in the world of fiction or in the theatre, all anyone knows of being a binman is that song of Lonnie Donnegan's, and let me tell you that if Lonnie Donnegan ever introduced himself to any of the binmen I worked with he'd have ended up at the bottom of twenty tons of landfill, the opinion they had of *My Old Man's a Dustman*.

There's a gap in the market for a serious novel on the life and loves of a binman, and because this is now what you know, and you should always write what you know, you fill that gap. You write the work that's been begging to be written.

You call it:

<u>Refuse</u>, by ***Brian Piddock***. 337 pages. 1985.

It's good. It's about an aspiring and brilliant writer who decides to throw off his middle-class roots and do the lowest menial job he can find, and the wretched world he discovers. It ends when in self defence he kills a jealous co-worker whose young and beautiful wife he is having an affair with. The ambiguity in the title — is it *'Refuse'* as in garbage, or *'Refuse'* as in 'won't do it' — is quite deliberate, and echoes the delicate wordplay throughout the book, in contrast with the crude characters the hero has to deal with.

No, frankly, let's be honest here. It's not good. No. It's *great*. Great is a word that shouldn't be over-used, but in this case it's easily justified. It puts those old novels about working people by such as Alan Sillitoe, John Braine, and Stan Barstow in the nursery. Now it'll be Sillitoe, Braine, Barstow, and Piddock. Or rather, Piddock (and Sillitoe, Braine, and Barstow). Never mind the Booker Prize, you're rehearsing your Nobel acceptance speech.

You send the manuscript to an agent, a carefully chosen and supremely lucky agent, whose fortune you are going to make. Unaccountably, within a couple of weeks there's not the phone call of congratulation and million pound offer, but it gets sent back. Some clerical error, no doubt. They'll be kicking themselves soon.

Never mind, someone else is in luck, and you send it to a different agent. They send it back. You try 30 agents, and each one returns it. Never mind, miss out the middle man, if they're that obtuse. You send it direct to a publisher. They send it back. 25 publishers, and they all send it back.

Never mind, your friends will read it and petition the publishing world until your masterpiece is printed. And the only thing your friends say, once they've read it, is that the dirty bits aren't dirty enough.

Broken, distraught, you put the manuscript in your desk drawer, on top of **The Dark Interloper** and **The Walking Wounded**.

But this one's different. It doesn't stay there, like **The Dark Interloper** or **The Walking Wounded**. Over the years you take it out to revise and rewrite it.

You make it less realistic and more satirical, and call it: **Giving the Dirt**. No one's interested. Then you make the satire broader, more humorous, almost slapstick. That's: **Get a Noseful!** Then the satire is eliminated, as the novel turns into a bleak portrait of working-class life: **Lords of Landfill**. The main character becomes black: **Dumped**. Then disabled: **Waste of Space**. Then a gay socialist drug addict: **Leftover Junk**.

After each revision, you send it off, and it comes back. And always there is the certainty in your mind that it's good, there is something there, something original and interesting, if only the right person would look at it at the right time. If only you could just give it the right spin. One more push, one more draft, and it's bound to be discovered.

Except, with every new draft and every new rejection, comes the nagging saying about good money chasing bad. Though in this case it's not money, it's time. It's your life.

You begin to think you should have burnt it nine years ago. Called it experience, practice, juvenilia. Think of what you might have written if you hadn't spent all that time on it! But it's too late. Every year, at least twice a year, you'll be walking home after a few pints of bitter and a couple of whisky chasers, thinking of something totally unrelated, those good mates of yours down the pub and their dinosaur left-wing political opinions, or whether there are any eggs in the house because you just fancy a fry up, and you'll see a wheely bin, and think: "A good novel about binning still hasn't been published."

Mainly because one hasn't been written. Except yours. And the idea occurs to you. Of course! The young wife who the hero has the affair with isn't married to one of the binmen. She *is* one of the binmen! Which solves the problem in the middle chapters. Which stresses the parallels between binning and warfare, especially in this modern age of female soldiers, making it a brilliant anti-war fable, especially if you bring it up to date and set it in the present world of new Labour and climate change.

You're gripped. You can't think of anything else. You've decided. You'll give it one last try.

On Monday morning, you look for the last draft. And you remember, it's in a box in the roof. Well now you look, it's three boxes, and you haven't written on the sides which one is the oldest and which the latest because when you put it upstairs you told yourself you'd never get it out again. Only sentimentality stopped you burning it, in fact.

You spend a week sorting out the various chapters, and the drafts, and you move a bit from here and a piece from there, and completely redo chapters 4 and 16, but not 12 because that's got some of your best writing, and you find that floppy disk which has the latest draft, but it will only work on your old Amstrad PCW9512 from ten years ago, which amazingly still works, and even has those old black and white games on it, which you try out for a few hours, and you have to go to the computer shop to get some sort of link between your laptop and the Amstrad, and after three whole days of trying you manage to copy the whole lot over, and you spend the rest of the month snipping and creating and renaming the characters, and you print the whole thing out, and you wrap it up and send it to a publisher, hoping it's not the same publisher you sent it to two years ago, but anyway you've given it a new name — **Smelling like Roses** — so they probably won't remember, and you sit back knowing this time you cracked it and all that effort was worth it.

Until it comes back, with hardly a comment.

They still don't like it, and you try again, and the second publisher, with obviously a more careful reader than the first, points out that people don't call them car phones anymore, they call them mobiles, and coal miners haven't been on strike for 20 years now because there aren't any coal miners, and you think: "How petty can you get?" but you realise, slowly, inevitably, that perhaps its time has passed, you don't know what the modern world of binning is like, there are probably swathes of business practice you're unfamiliar with, recycling, different lorries, new types of bin, it's too late.

Too late.

The saddest realisation. It's a great book, and should have been seen as such, but it's too late.

So draft 16 gets bunged back in the boxes along with drafts 1 to 15, and shoved in the loft again, and you wonder, Why don't I learn? Why do I waste time on it? Why don't I just make a big bonfire out of it?

And then comes the saving idea.

There is some use to those years of work, those reams of paper, beyond increasing the carbon dioxide level in the world.

You may not have succeeded in writing the ultimate bin-man novel.

But you know what you can succeed in.

You can write:

A *How To Write Book*.

chapter three

Choosing your subject

Let's recap: you decided, early in your life, that what you
wanted to be — no! What you *were* — was a writer. You
wrote two good novels, apprentice works, as it were, and adapted one for the stage. You wrote a third, a very decent novel,
when you were not long out of college. You did a year at a
teacher training college. You became a maths teacher, for the
long tempting holidays when you need do nothing except
write. You met your lovely wife, Laura, at a New Year's Eve
party when you both ended up in bed together but too drunk
to do anything. Despite that, you had two gorgeous children,
Adam and Jordan.

FACT BOX 6

Let's recap – always a useful phrase, as it allows you to
repeat anything you've just said. You must assume the
reader has a short memory, or is so lazy and feckless he or
she can't be bothered to read the detail. Of course, I would
never assume you are like that.
To recap: recap.

The knowledge that your destiny is to be a writer, one of
the greats, has never left you, despite the years of fiddling with
your last work, and you can't stop fiddling with the bloody
thing, and however much you fiddle with the bloody thing, no
one seems interested in putting it into print.

So what are you to do? Do you vow that the only writing
you ever do from now on will be the words on the cheque that

pays the milk bill? Do you go into the garage, shut the door, and turn on the car engine and wait for the fumes to take you away from this world of despair, where youthful hopes and dreams get trampled on by the monsters of malice and jealousy?

Of course not!

There's one last avenue you can drive your precious baby down. You may not win the Nobel prize for literature, but it's better than having her rot on the loft beams.

To the rescue come:

How To Write Books!

You know about binning. That's your personal experience. Even better, you know about writing about binning. You were a binman for a mere six weeks. You've been a binman novelist for 10 years. There's nothing you don't know about writing a novel about binning. If you went on Mastermind it would be your specialist subject. In fact, you'd know more than the question setter. You would have to be the question setter!

You must use your expertise. The world needs it.

Of course, **How To Write A Binning Novel** wouldn't have sold many copies. Especially since the greatest novel about binning couldn't get into print. I had to widen the territory. And so I decided to create: **How To Write A Novel About Modern Working-Class Life** by **Brian Piddock**.

What enjoyment that writing was. What bliss. I could use plot examples from all 16 drafts of **Smelling Like Roses**. I had 10 titles, of varying strength. There were at least six different styles, from comical to naturalistic. It was like creating freshly squeezed orange juice. The pulp was thrown away, and only the tasty bits left. I looked in the library for a few How To Write Book publishers, and at only the fourth attempt received the letter we all pray for. They liked my book!

And after only a few rewrites, and proof checking, and a year, came that happy and glorious moment. The publication of:

How To Write A Novel About Modern Working-Class Life, by **Brian Piddock**. 152 pages. 1990. Crocker & Thistle.

Obviously I have a great affection for *How To Write A Novel About Modern Working-Class Life*. It was my first work in print, and while I had some questions over the cover, rather gaudy, I thought, and not quite expressing the finesse of the work within, I have to say it sold very well indeed. It had a reprint, an indication of the demand. In fact, I believe that work of mine was single-handedly responsible for the revival of novels about the working-class. Perhaps Jack Bryce's *Canteen Antics* and Barry Barker's *Hot Flesh In Cold Storage*, which clearly show the influence of *How To Write A Novel About Modern Working-Class Life*, haven't the fame or resilience of Alan Sillitoe's *Saturday Night And Sunday Morning* or Stan Barstow's *A Kind Of Loving*, but they are not bad books, not by any means. Not necessarily better than *Smelling Like Roses*, not at all, certainly not, but better than they would have been if they hadn't read my book, even if no acknowledgement was made. But the How To Write writer doesn't look for public acknowledgement. It's the silent acknowledgement that does the trick. Especially the silent cheque, every six months.

But what you want to know is, what are you going to write about? I suspect you may have been on the Amazon website and typed in their search engine "*how to write*" and perhaps been a little daunted to discover 1583 results (and now, with this book, 1584). Surely, you think, everything that can be covered has been covered.

This is negative thinking, and I refuse to allow it in this book, or any of my books.

Listen: I've had my share of downs. More than my fair share. I've had huge disappointments and bad luck. I've seen lesser talents than myself succeed. I have been despised as a failure. Fortune, sometimes, hasn't crossed the road to be on the other side from me. She's caught the easyJet plane to Marrakech so as not to be in the same continent.

But I've never indulged in negative thinking. It's not in my make up, and it shouldn't be in yours.

Let me give you an example, to show how far negative thinking is from being in my make up.

There was a girl I knew at college, back in the 80s. Her name was Diane. She was a particularly lovely girl, but she had a particularly loathsome boyfriend called Kurt. He was one of those sneering giggling macho rugby-playing types (I've always preferred football, personally) (not to play, of course, but to watch) (on the television, anyway). I knew that the only reason Diane went out with Kurt was a lack of self-esteem. There could be no other reason. He had no virtues apart from an ability to drink a great deal of beer and thump people's noses on the rugby field and make acid comments about anyone who wasn't in his inner circle of friends.

He was also a hypocrite of the first order, because if ever Diane threatened to leave him when he behaved badly towards her, as he frequently did, he would become meek and apologetic and promise to be nice to her.

I know this because Diane spent long hours with me, pouring out her troubles. I was, and am, a good listener. It's important, as a writer.

FACT BOX 7

A h, those golden, innocent days when I was at university, where no one was deceitful or malicious or jealous, and we all spoke honestly and directly with each other, because, basically, we all had a great love for each other. Very happy days they were for me.

However much I wanted to, I didn't say to her: "Leave this oaf. You'll never be happy with him." I just made sure I was always there, if she needed me.

I also pretended to be Kurt's greatest friend. I endured his stupid rugby drinking games in the bar, the forfeits, the sniggering, the humiliations.

And one evening, when he was well and truly sozzled, I casually mentioned to him how a certain girl I knew fancied him.

"Really? What's she like? Is she good looking?" was his pathetic response.

Extremely good-looking, I assured him.

"But I love Diane," he said, hiccupping. "I'm going to marry Diane. She's the only girl for me."

I knew this was only drunken self-deceit, and I worked hard on Lorraine, who shagged anything remotely masculine, by describing the legends of Kurt's sexual prowess (another demonstration of my talent for making up stories).

One evening, in the student union bar, when I knew Diane had gone home for the weekend, and Kurt had had a few beers, and everything was primed and ready, I managed to introduce Kurt to Lorraine. The result was phenomenal.

I almost felt sorry for Kurt, as he disappeared down the stairs, dragged by Lorraine's large paw.

Of course it was absolutely vital that, first, Diane shouldn't realise I had anything to do with fixing Kurt up with Lorraine, and second she shouldn't find out from me what had happened between Kurt and Lorraine. This wasn't easy to engineer, but was an early display for me of my skill in plotting (which I later put to good use when I thought about my second How To Write Book, *How To Write A Really Good Crime Plot*).

I told the story of Kurt and Lorraine's night of passion to a boy who was the boyfriend of a girl who wasn't friends with Diane but was friends with someone who was, and within a day Diane had come running and weeping to me. Well, I happened to pass near her room, and knocked on her door, and discovered her weeping.

I was overjoyed. I was also very careful. I took Kurt's side. Perhaps she was wrong. She shouldn't listen to gossip. Kurt wouldn't do a thing like that, he's a nice guy, and besides I saw him that evening and I didn't remember him going off with any girl.

I almost played that too well, she was beginning to believe me, so I had to rescue the situation by suggesting she talked to a girl who had a room opposite Lorraine's, so that she could see how ridiculous she was being, accusing that fine boyfriend of hers.

Everything came in like the brilliant final chapter of the detective novel I've thought about writing for years. Kurt was exposed and Diane was desolate. All I had to do was be there for her, and wait.

Then, disaster struck.

It wouldn't be allowed in a crime novel, or a thriller. You'll have noticed, a point I shall certainly make if I ever get round to writing **How To Write A Really Good Crime Plot**, the hero gets the girl. Because during the novel there may be death, grisly as you like, but at the end the reader must feel safe. There may be a torturer on the loose, but he or she only tortures people we either don't know or don't care about. We care about the hero. We care about the girl. They are going to be all right. And they are going to be together.

FACT BOX 8

Polite warning: though I didn't write **How To Write A Really Good Crime Plot**, I might, one day, and since I've mentioned it here, it's my title, and my copyright. This goes for anything else I mention. Just so you know! Like I said, it's a tough business and you can never be too careful.

That's not how it is in real life.

In real life, I got tonsillitis.

I could hardly breathe. I had to go to the Health Centre for a week. And when the antibiotics had done their job and I was allowed back to my room, Diane was going out with Howard, a postgraduate in Ancient History.

I often saw them together, but I hardly ever spoke to Diane.

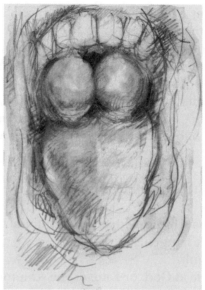

The ravages of tonsilitis *

Well, I tried, but something had happened and she rather snubbed me. I don't think it was anything I had done, it was that she now perceived me as inferior, being merely a second year undergraduate.

Now at this point I could have broken down completely. I had considered Diane to be the only person I would ever love. Of course that turned out not to be true, but when you're at that age feelings seem to be permanent. An illness, that I had never had before, and could have struck at any time, struck at

---

* I have to agree that this is what it felt like, though I don't believe it's an entirely accurate portrayal of the medical effects of that particular condition. But of course I'm forgetting, young Anthony is an artist, and he has that little bit of paper that allows him to stretch the truth.
(He's using artistic licence, is what I'm getting at)
(Sorry to spell it out, I'm sure you understood that, but some people won't, they're not as well educated as you are)

the one moment I needed to be fit and well, and able to ask Diane to go with me on a trip to the park, or the seaside, to take her mind off things. We could have strolled on the beach. Gone to a café and laughed at the old people. Sat on the train home, close, tired, together.

I often wonder what would have happened, where I would be now, if I hadn't had tonsillitis, and I'd married Diane.

We'd have had lots of children. She was wonderful with children.

I imagine.

We wouldn't have argued. She wasn't the argumentative sort.

We would have been happy, going into our old age.

But it didn't happen.

Nobody's fault.

I didn't curse at God, or Fate, or the streptococcus bacteria.

I poured my heart out into a short story called **Sick With Desire**. It was writing as therapy, true, but there's nothing wrong with that, because I was writing what I knew (see *Rule 1*, **Write what you know**). For five years in the 80s, I sent it to *Woman's Own*, then *Woman*, then *Woman's Weekly*, then *Woman And Home*.

They didn't like it, I don't know why not, so in 1988 I brought it up to date and for a slightly less mature audience rewrote it as **The Tonsils Of Love**, for *19*, then *Bliss*, *Sugar* and *Mizz*. They didn't like it either, the fools.

In 1991 I let loose, and reworked it as **Hot Fevers** for *Mayfair*, *The Erotic Review*, *Penthouse*, and *Big Busters* (I had to do a lot of unpleasant research by reading these magazines as, naturally, I would never normally look at them). No one liked it.

But it didn't matter to me, because by 1994 I was a published author, and used the story of Diane and me as the basis for my:

How To Write An Erotic Romantic Short Story, by Brian Piddock. 113 pages. 1996. The Modesty Press.

Now this present volume isn't a self-help book. Not in the *How To Live Without Anger*, or *How To Live With Success*, kind of book. This is a book on writing, not living. Except that the true writer lives his life by writing. I know I do.

FACT BOX 9

Though if you're interested in those works, and think you'd like to try and write your own, drop a note to the publishers of this volume, and suggest they commission me to write a **How To Write A How To Live Book**. I could do it.

But I think my example shows how to get over those little, or large, disappointments of life. In fact, let's be honest, if we had no disappointments, if everything went well, if I was living in bliss with Diane and the grandchildren in that cottage in the country, what would I write about? Maybe the odd article in *Country Living*, or *Homes And Gardens*, but that would hardly pay the rent.

Even if, in those circumstances, fame and money would mean nothing to me.

chapter four

Categories

What you wanted to know was what you're going to write about.

So now I shall tell you.

Well, not tell, I'm not here to tell. I suggest. I advise. You have to do some of the work, for goodness sake.

Let's look more closely at those 1583 How To Write Books that Amazon has in stock or usually dispatches within 4 to 6 weeks.

Let's put them into two categories:

Category 1.

And:

Category 2.

Now we've done that, let's define those categories a little more precisely:

Category 1 — common or obvious subjects.

And:

Category 2 — unusual or obscure subjects.

Category 1 (which I'll call a How To Write a Category 1 Book for convenience) — common or obvious subjects — includes *How To Write A Thriller, How To Write For Children, How To Write A Letter*.

Category 2 (which I'll call a How To Write a Category 2 Book for convenience) — unusual or obscure subjects — includes *How To Write for the Psion 9, How To Write a Training Manual for Large Plant and Machinery, How To Write a Historical Novel about Poor Serving Girls in 19th Century Northumberland*.

I feel quite confident in asserting that no book spans both categories. Except — uniquely and extraordinarily — one.
This one!

How To Write a Category 1 Book

You like thrillers, let's say. You've read several, on the bus or train or tube. You've watched how gripped other people seem to be as they sit with their John Grisham or Dan Brown, the world around them lost. Leonardo da Vinci could fly past the window in his helicopter, and they wouldn't notice. This is the genre you want to write, so you can grip people as Brown and Grisham grip them.

You note that 90% of the effect of the book is in the first couple of sentences. You make a few attempts.

> *Jim Daniels cowered on the ground as the gunman pointed the revolver to his head.*
> *"But why?" cried Jim. "Just tell me why!"*

Or:

> *Jeff Rawlinson thought he was incredibly lucky to get a lift in the smart new BMW, after he'd broken down on the M6. What neither Jeff nor the driver knew was that there was a bomb under the BMW,*

timed to go off in precisely 20 minutes — and the driver didn't intend to stop until he got to London.

You've thought of a plot:

The US government is being taken over, one by one, by Chinese agents who have undergone plastic surgery. Only the hero knows this. But who will believe him, especially when he's arrested and put in solitary confinement in the most secure prison in the world?

Or:

Terrorists plant a nuclear device in the House of Commons. It will go off at the opening of Parliament. Only the hero can discover the plot, but can he do so in time, especially when at the moment he's halfway up the North Ridge of Everest?

You've even discovered what sort of person the hero should be. He should be handsome, learned, sensitive, strong. His wife died in tragic circumstances he couldn't have prevented, so he's now free to love the heroine (he has to have been married, or everyone would think he was gay, which is not allowed). He has an expert knowledge in the required field, dendrochronology or Renaissance architecture, so only he can save the government/city/world/universe.

You are now ready to put pen to paper.

You are about to write:

How To Write a Thriller.

Unfortunately, you look at the list on Amazon. There is already a book called *How To Write a Thriller*. There is also a book called *How To Write a Better Thriller*. Also *How To Write Exciting Thrillers*. *How To Write Block-Busting Thrillers*. *How To Write Best-Selling Thrillers*. *How To Write Best-Selling Block-Busting Thrillers*. Surely, there is no room and no demand for yet one more book on the subject.

Nonsense!

To demonstrate this fallacy, I have devised a simple graph:

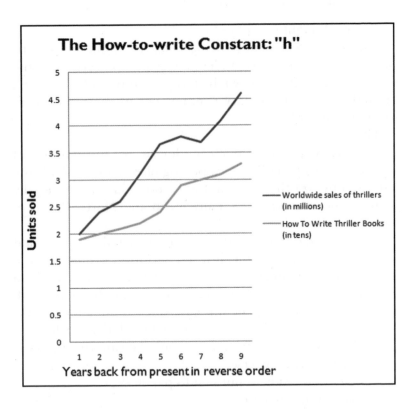

The x-axis shows the worldwide yearly sales for the last ten years of thrillers and How To Write a Thriller books. And we can easily see that there is a direct and obvious correlation.

I call this number:

"**h**" (where any genre sold equals the number of How To Write Genre Books in publication at any one time).

"**h**" is the How To Write writers' Cosmological Constant. It is our guiding light. Without it, we are blind.

After years of experience and thought and work deep into the night with chalk and blackboard and mathematical computer programs, as both a How To Write writer and a teacher of mathematics, I have finally formulated and computated the magic figure, and can now reveal to you:

h equals 0.0000013.

(with a margin of plus or minus 0.000005).

In other words, if 4 million thrillers are shifted in any one year, then the market can sustain 26 How To Write a Thriller Books in that year.

FACT BOX 10

There is a rival theory, espoused by my great friend and fellow How To Write writer, Ryan Jinks. Ryan calls his constant 'm', and divides it by the number of new books of a particular genre published in any one year. I have long argued with him over this, and remain convinced that the sale of books is a far more reliable figure, being absolute, than the number of books published, especially when the latter figure takes no account of books that fail to sell more than a paltry 2,000 copies, such as, for example, his own Death's Door, published in 1993 by Pinkertons & Son. Of course, we joke that without the resounding failure of Death's Door, Ryan would not have become the How To Write writer he is now! It is a topic of ceaseless amusement in the pub.

For those interested, he considers that 'm' equals 0.35.

If you're finding all these mathematical formulae confusing, and I taught maths for long enough to recognise those shifting-in-the-seat blank looks, because I used to get enough of those no matter how carefully I used chalk and words of one syllable so that even an average orang-utan should have been able to comprehend the simultaneous equation, then let me put it more simply:

There's always room for another How To Write Book.

And nothing is simpler than that — except for Ryan's maths!

You've looked at the list and seen there's a *How To Write a Thriller, How To Write a Better Thriller, How To Write a Block-Busting Thriller, How To Write a Best-Selling Thriller, How To Write a Block-Busting Best-Selling Thriller*.

Well, you're just going to have to improve on those titles, and write the ultimate How To Write a Thriller Book. In fact, I don't believe there is a *How To Write An Ultimate Thriller*. Or even an *Ultimate How To Write a Thriller*.

What's more, you're at an advantage. Some poor sucker wanders into a bookshop, desperate for a book that will make his name and fortune, because he's read *The Da Vinci Code* and *The Last Juror*, and he knows he can do better, and he's got this great idea, it's like the end of the world unless his hero can defeat the wicked Uzbeks, and all he's got to do is just write it out, basically it tells itself, he just needs one or two pointers.

So what does he buy? *How To Write a Thriller?* That seems to be what's required, but hang on. He sees *How To Write a Better Thriller*. Well that's what he wants, not just to write a thriller, but a better thriller. The best, in fact. And at that moment he notices, amazingly, *How To Write The Best Thriller*. That's for him. Except he then spots *How To Write a Best-Selling Thriller*. Well, it's not quality he's after so much as giving up his job as a NatWest cashier and buying a penthouse in the City of London, so it had better be that.

Until he catches sight of:

How To Write The Best Ultimate Best-Selling Thriller.

And seeing there is nothing to cap that, that's the one he buys, gleeful and happy, and all the others get dusty and remaindered and pulped.

In fact I realised a long time ago that if you're not first in the queue, and you didn't write *How To Write a Thriller* — because a lot of stolid citizens will always go for that title, feeling it has the weight of simplicity — then don't bother with the middling titles, the Better Book, or The Book That Sells, or The Best-Selling Book. They will end up in the middle of the queue, and the middle of the queue doesn't move, it's like those hitchhiking queues I used to join when I was a student,

30 people at a motorway service station, and the only one likely to get a lift was the one at the front and the one at the back and all the rest had no chance.

FACT BOX 11

Whatever happened to students hitchhiking? I used to love it. You met such interesting people. I remember once, when I was a callow lad of 19, being given a lift in a sports car, and 100 yards down the road was another person hitching, a rather attractive girl. Luckily he didn't throw me out, which I feared, but let her in as well, so she had to sit on my knees for the journey. I thought it was the most thrilling experience of my life, that beautiful girl so close to me, until after about ten miles I got cramp and had to beg the driver to stop.

We had a bit of an argument then, the three of us, as to who was going to be left by the side of the road, but as I had the priority of being the first passenger into the car I was surprised to discover that I was the one dumped out in the rain in an awful spot on the A1, and had to walk about five miles to a town, where I could get a bus.

All good experience, and what a shame that today's youth aren't getting the chance to do similar research into life's interesting oddities.

To recap: with a How To Write a Category 1 Book, if you're not first, go for the biggest title you can. How To Write the Perfect/Superlative/Most Excellent.

And if you think that might put off Joe or Josephine Public, who don't even know what superlative means, let alone have the arrogance to consider they could write it, then tempt them with greed:

How To Write a Money Spinning Thriller.
How To Make Lots of Money by Writing a Thriller.
How To Write a Thriller and Win The Lottery.

FACT BOX 12

This book's a case in point. If there was already a **How To Write a How To Write Book** I'd have to jump the queue and call it **How To Write The Perfect How To Write Book**.
Which it is, of course.

With a little imagination it's possible to cap everyone else's work with yours.

Remember, with a Category 1 How To Write Book, you have to be number one!

chapter five

Categories (2) (category 2)

How To Write Category 2 Books are slightly different. Easier, in many ways, though the risks are greater. The competition may be smaller, but so is the market.

This is what I had to think long and hard about with both my *How To Write a Novel About Modern Working-Class Life*, and *How To Write an Erotic Romantic Short Story*.

Let's take *How To Write a Novel About Modern Working-Class Life*. There are a surprising number of aspiring working-class novelists around. I met one or two at university, and have since met several more. The trouble is, they're not open to advice, generally. They think they know it all.

Like Wes.

Wes had worked his way up through secondary modern school to college, and scraped enough A-levels to get to university, and he wasn't going to let anyone tell him how to write anything. I remember one night in the bar, in our second year at university, well before my writing career took off, he mentioned to me that he was writing a novel about his early life in Erdington. I suggested he looked at *Room At The Top*, and *The Loneliness Of The Long-Distance Runner*, for a few pointers in the right direction. He said, and I always remember this, because Wes was a marvellously cogent speaker:

"I don't need to look at other people's books. Books aren't life, you middle-class tosser."

I didn't ask him what he was doing at university, sitting an English degree, if he thought he didn't need to look at other people's books, because as well as a direct way of speaking he had a rather violent temper.

But that's the kind of person I was up against when I began

planning out my book. They believe they don't need a How To Write book. They believe they can just write it. Needless to say, Wes never, as far as I'm aware, published his opus, though he did have some success later as a merchant banker. I often wish I hadn't lost contact with him, as I'm sure he could have provided me with lots of useful research for a *How To Write a Novel about the Inner Workings of the City*. Actually, for all his rough edges, I grew to become rather fond of Wes. I learned from him many useful things, how to play table football, how to belch, though I could never quite master his greatest skill: how to pull any girl he fancied.

It was amazing to watch him at work, because he didn't need to work. They came to him, but at least I could pick up the crumbs that Wes left behind. Well, once I did, anyway, when he said I could talk to the friend of the girl he was after, since he "didn't fancy a threesome tonight since I'm a bit bloody knackered".

What a great bloke. And we had some really wonderful times together, Wes and me. It was a shame our very close friendship ended the way it did. But I have to say that him sleeping with my girlfriend was frankly unforgivable. I mean having no morality is one thing but having no loyalty quite another.

She was a lovely girl, too, Sue was. I had even thought she and I might marry. So I suppose Wes helped, in that he showed me what she was really like.

I suppose really, thinking about it, I shouldn't have been so resentful with him that I trashed his room, even if he deserved it. Apart from it being an extremely dangerous thing to do with Wes. Although, fair dos and all credit to him, he didn't trash my room back, and that shows the sort of great guy he was, not to return an eye for an eye.

No, he trashed me instead, good and proper. I was hardly able to breathe for a week. Still, at least that was an honest working-class response.

Yes, a really great guy, Wes. I wish he was still my friend. If you happen to read this, Wes, and recognise yourself, I forgive you, mate! And maybe you can give me back that tenner I lent you in 1983 (now worth about £100 in today's terms). Only kidding, though I bet you're raking it in, merchant banker, what a lucky bastard! Ever considered buying up a publishing firm with your spare change? If so, let me know, won't you?

Wes, Brian's best mate *

So, most putative working-class novelists, like Wes, would refuse to read my invaluable advice. And many other putative working-class novelists would scarcely be able to read my invaluable advice, or would have to look up 'putative' in the dictionary. If they knew what a dictionary was.

But that was fine, because that wasn't my market. ***How To Write a Novel About Modern Working-Class Life*** wasn't aimed at

---

* *Except the girls Wes went for didn't look like they were out of Jane Austen. Out of an Austin Mini Cooper, more like. And they all wore very short skirts. And they were beautiful. Every one of them. Oh God, I thought, how does he do it?*

working-class novelists. It was aimed at people writing a working-class novel, and just as Hemingway didn't need to be a
Spanish matador to write about bullfighting, you don't need to
be working-class to write a working-class novel. In my case, a
six-week disgusting stint in the messy job of binning was more
than enough. As I suggest in **How To Write a Novel About
Modern Working-Class Life**, watching a documentary on BBC2
will probably do for gaining enough knowledge on the subject.

So my market was potentially huge. All those sons and
daughters of teachers or doctors who have spent the summer
holidays working in a warehouse or digging up the roads, or
simply like to go to a good local's pub (like my own Golden
Lion, where I've spent many a Saturday night discussing the
football results with gnarled old workers from the nearby tin
can factory), and feel that the experience ought to be put down
on paper.

Better still, all those middle-class people who are the ones
best able to write about working-class life have no fear or
shame about getting all the information they can about tips or
shortcuts — after all, that's why they're successful and middle-
class.

So why did **How To Write a Novel About Modern Working-
Class Life** only sell 154 copies?

It was — and I can't stress enough the importance of this
— the *title* that was at fault. The title wasn't clear, and you
should always have a clear title. Assume that people, even people in bookshops, are stupid. I knew what the book was about,
it was about Sillitoe and Braine and Barstow, and dragging
them into the 21st Century. Well, 20th, when I wrote it. And
Jack Bryce and Barry Barker understood that, obviously, you
can tell by *Canteen Antics* and *Hot Flesh In Cold Storage* (a letter
would have been nice, just a little word: "Thanks, Brian, for
showing me how to do it." Or a mention on their publishers'
web sites. But no, nothing. That's the writing world for you).
But evidently others didn't understand the title, or they'd have
bought the book.

Get the title right, and you're three-quarters of the way to a bestseller.

Of course, I shouldn't knock **How To Write a Novel About Modern Working-Class Life**. As I said before, its influence was huge, far more than its limited sales, and it made my name in the genre. It was my *Love Me Do*. It didn't get to number one, but you'd be amazed how many people have said it's their favourite amongst all my work.

FACT BOX 13

Not that 154 copies is a complete disaster in the How To Write world (even if 62 of those 154 were books that I sold to my friends, family and neighbours at such a reduced price that I made a loss on each one). It may not be as many as the average Danielle Steel or Jackie Collins, obviously, but then my readership is considerably more exclusive than Steel's or Collins'. I would like to think that all of those 154 people are members of a very special family. Besides, I haven't seen the figures, but I can't imagine that a certain Writing a Social Science Dissertation could have sold any more. How many social scientists are there? And how many of those need someone to tell them how to write a dissertation? And how did he persuade any of his friends, family and neighbours to buy such an unappealing title? Good old Ryan, eh.

Or, let's consider **How To Write an Erotic Romantic Short Story**. If **How To Write a Novel About Modern Working-Class Life** was my *Love Me Do*, **How To Write an Erotic Romantic Short Story** was my *Magical Mystery Tour*. People didn't quite get it.

I know my publishers Crocker & Thistle didn't, at first, God bless them. **How To Write a Novel About Modern Working-Class Life** was doing moderately well, had been reviewed favourably in one or two prestigious writers' magazines, was bubbling under, there or thereabouts, and they were keen to see my second work. Now, the second work is always considered the tricky one. In fact, there's another rule:

RULE 2
For your second work, never just pick out of your drawer the book that's been rejected 50 times and which you wrote before your first published book.

You know the one I mean, it's really your first book, and it's a cardinal error to get it out, blow the dust off it, shove it in an envelope, just send it off, and think that'll do. That's lazy, and publishers, who are not idiots, will see right through you, and if they are worth their salt will send it back to you with a cursory and curt note of rejection.

No, never ever do that.

Always, always, print it out again, and then send it off to the publishers.

That old copy, in the bottom drawer, will have egg stains, and bent corners, and a doodle where a previous publisher's reader needed some blank paper for the anagram in his crossword.

Buy a fresh ream of paper — a ream only costs about £2, for goodness sake, and a new cartridge for the inkjet is only a fiver, I mean a compatible will do — and print it all off. They'll never know it's an ancient work, even if they were one of the publishers who rejected it five years ago, because they see so many books they don't read them, they only read the title (importance of, again!), and the first and last pages.

No, the fact that *How To Write an Erotic Romantic Short Story* was my first effort and I was pretending it was my second wasn't the problem. It was the genre. Are there, Mr Charles Vick of Crocker & Thistle asked, erotic romantic short stories? And if there are, who publishes them? *The Erotic Review* and *Mayfair* and *Big Busters* print erotic stories, *Woman* and *Woman's Own* print romantic stories. Who prints erotic romantic short stories? No one does.

Well I knew that. It's why I couldn't get my story about

Diane and me published in the first place, because there was nowhere to get it published. It was why **How To Write An Erotic Romantic Short Story** had been rejected in the first place, too. But that was over five years ago, and I thought times would have changed and the publishing world caught up with a pioneer like me, and there would now be a magazine that published erotic romantic short stories.

Furthermore, since I was now a published author, I considered that after the success of **How To Write a Novel About Modern Working-Class Life** I could be influential enough to create the market. Single handed I had recreated the working-class novel. Now I would force magazines in being to cater for my story about Diane and me, and at long long last it would appear in print!

Crocker & Thistle didn't see it that way. Well, I told them if they didn't take it exactly as it was, title and all, I'd go elsewhere, and a lot of editors I had met were begging me to give them my next work.

This was, in fact, a bluff, but sometimes you have to be ruthless in this business. They'll be ruthless with you, have no fear about that. Any tactic is legitimate, frankly, if it works.

In the case of **How To Write an Erotic Romantic Short Story**, it didn't work. Charles Vick invited me to offer it else-

---

FACT BOX 14

If you're one of the unlucky ones not to be privileged enough to read **How To Write an Erotic Romantic Short Story**, *perhaps you too feel unsure that there is a market for erotic romantic short stories. Let me assure you, if you could read* **Sick With Desire** *you would be convinced. It's touching, exciting, thrilling, heartwarming, sensuous, intense, emotional, sexual, poignant, touching, and triumphant. And no, none of it is fantasy, but all of it the untarnished and unvarnished truth about the affair that Diane and I had. Or would have had, if things had gone right for us.*

---

where, because in his opinion there wasn't a market for the book, and I told him, in one of the most satisfying letters I have ever written, where to go. I told him what a mistake he was making. I told him that he could stuff his opinion up an orifice which I won't mention here, but which I specified quite exactly in my letter. Suffice to say it would cause him some pain if he had taken me literally. I would soon buy out his pitiful firm, sack the lot of them, and dedicate them to publishing only my work.

He didn't reply.

He had invited me to offer it elsewhere, and I offered it everywhere, and nowhere did they want it. Eventually I was forced to offer it to the vanity publishers, *The Modesty Press*. Now if you read any How To Write a book you'll have been told:

RULE 3
Never ever deal with a vanity publisher. It'll cost you a lot of money, you'll get five copies, and the other thousand will never leave the warehouse.

Nonsense. Rubbish. They lie! It really doesn't matter what sort of small fortune it costs (every penny of the royalties from *How To Write a Novel About Modern Working-Class Life* three times over, in my case). It really doesn't matter that they won't sell a single copy and you'll end up giving it away to your friends because it was printed on such shabby paper you can't wrap chips with it.

It's your baby. And it's in book form. It's got your name and the title on the front (even if they can't spell 'Piddock', or 'erotic'). It's got your words on the inside (in more or less the right order, except for chapter 3 being where chapter 1 should be and chapter 6 being blank and chapter 11 missing). And that's all that matters.

However, there is a lesson to be learned here. A How To Write a Category 2 book is not just a matter of making up a genre. Look back at my definition of a Category 2 book:

Category 2 — unusual or obscure subjects.

Now, obscure and unusual is not the same as "not in existence". Nothing is certain in the How To Write world, but I suspect *How To Write a Curriculum Vitae in Blank Verse* might not meet favour with many publishers or readers. Nor *How To Write An Experimental Novel for Toddlers*.

Which leads us neatly on to yet another rule:

RULE 4
Know your market!

This doesn't mean to say there aren't plenty of gaps waiting to be filled.

For example, in the academic sphere, and almost a quarter of all How To Write books are in the academic sphere, there are still books to be written. Is there a *How To Write a Thesis in Media Studies* (assuming that anyone who does Media Studies writes anything, as opposed to sitting and watching television all the time)? What about *How To Write an Essay for African Diasporean Studies*, if that's your bag?

But be quick. Perhaps before this book has been published there may be a *How To Write a Thesis in Media Studies* or *How To Write an Essay for African Diasporean Studies*, and I wouldn't recommend the Category 1 strategy of calling your work *How To Write a Better Thesis for Media Studies* or *How To Write a Block-Busting Essay for African Diasporean Studies*, although this may do as a last resort.

Then there's the Category 2 sub genre of How To Write books that are not about books at all. Examples:

How To Write a Wedding Speech for a Previously Married and Divorced Couple.

How To Write Damning Teacher's Comments at the Bottom of Pupils' Essays.

How To Write a Good Discussion of Last Night's TV Programme.

How To Write Witticisms to Keep a Long Raffle Draw Interesting.

And before you tell me these are far too specific, I would just like to say that last night in the pub I mentioned all these topics and a great majority of those present agreed that they were necessary and useful subjects for many people, even if they wouldn't buy them themselves. But then if you've ever tried to get any of them down my pub to buy their round you would hope they're not typical of the spending public (only kidding, chaps!).

There are, in short, a huge number of category 2 subjects waiting to be written about. And what's more, in today's multimedia world, anyone can be an author. Think you know how to write a shopping list? Write a How To Write a book about it! You have money problems and have to write a letter to the bank at least once a month to ask for a bigger overdraft, apologise for going over the limit, or threaten to take your business elsewhere because of their swingeing returned direct debit fees? Write a How To Write book about it!

And you will have money problems. People think that every How To Write writer is raking in JK Rowling-type royalties. No How To Write writer is rich, let me assure you. Apart from my good mate Ryan Jinks, of course, and no one knows how he got his money, though some amazing rumours fly around. However he got it, he's still last to the bar, though.

FACT BOX 15

He's got a wonderful technique, Ryan, for avoiding buying a round. When entering a pub with a group, if he finds himself leading the way to the door, easy, he opens the door for everyone else to go in so he'll be last at the bar. If he finds he's second, and someone else as canny as him opens the door so Ryan is now first to the bar, he suddenly finds he has to go to the loo, or do up his shoelace, or there's someone he must say hello to first.

A true master at not putting his hand in his pocket, is Ryan!

That's a How To Write writer for you. We have lots of useful discussions in the pub, Ryan and I. Some of my best ideas have come in the pub, chatting to Ryan. And those ideas have gone out of the pub when he's taken them home with him! Only kidding. How To Write writers need fellow How To Write writers to talk to, because only the How To Write writer understands the pain and problems a fellow How To Write writer has.

When I published my **How To Write An Erotic Romantic Short Story** I was staring into a black hole. *The Modesty Press* charged me thousands, and I got back about £10. I was married by then, of course, but I think most How To Write writers will admit that their spouses are not the best people to turn to for advice, especially when the problems involve the investment of several thousand pounds into the buying of badly printed toilet paper.

We weren't long married at that time, Laura and I, and very much in love. She was doing a little occasional job in a factory, I was teaching, but had changed to part-time as I had every confidence my writing would take off.

I can still remember those awful mornings waiting for the post. I had just completed my third work, and had sent it out. Every day as I heard the letters fall onto the hall floor, I would rush to see if a publisher had accepted it, only to find either the returned manuscript, or another letter from the bank reminding us that our overdraft limit had been exceeded once again. Or, on more than one occasion, as I seemed to remember, both events happening with the same delivery.

But I knew then, as I know now, the How To Write writer's lot is not an easy one. Unless, like Ryan, you're remarkably lucky.

Let's sum up this chapter and the previous one, perhaps the most important in the book (apart from chapters 2, 8, 11 and 15, of course):

1   Know which category your book comes under.
2   If it's Category 1, make it the best Category 1 title there can possibly be.
3   If it's Category 2, make sure it's not so obscure no one's interested.

FACT BOX 16

Of course, you can even invent your own category. We've had Lad-lit, which is meant to appeal to young men and is all about them getting drunk and going on holiday and having rampant sex with young women (I imagine, I've never actually read any of these books, thank God). We've had Chick-lit, which is meant to appeal to young women and is all about them getting drunk and going on holiday and having rampant sex not with young men who read Lad-lit but with Greek waiters. And now there's Mum-lit, about women with children and the women get drunk and go on holiday and have rampant sex with Greek waiters (I wouldn't go near one of those books either). So what about Dad-lit, for example? Which might be about some man getting drunk and going on holiday and having rampant sex with Greek waiters. No. Sorry. Waitresses. Not waiters.

Not unless it's Gay-dad-lit.

Or you could rebel against the whole sequence of categories and invent one called Un-lit, which is about people not getting drunk or going on holiday or having rampant sex with Greek waiters. Or Dimly-lit, about people too stupid even to get drunk and go on holiday and have rampant sex with Greek waiters.

---

4   If you really want to write your How To Write book, then ignore rule 3.

5   Ignore rule 4 if it means spending money. You'll hate your self, believe me, and your wife will hate you even more.

6   Ignore rule 5 if your name is Ryan Jinks and you're very rich!

chapter six

Study the genre

Studying the genre is obvious, really. It's one of the great commandments, along with *Write what you know about* and *Never ever deal with a vanity publisher*.

RULE 5
You can't write a How to Write book unless you've read other How to Write books.

You should have known that. Do I have to do everything for you? I've led you to the river, but do I really have to push your head in before you realise that water is in front of you?

You wouldn't try and fit a radiator without watching a plumber or looking in a plumbing book, would you? But writing's different, of course, isn't it? Just start tapping on the keys.

It makes me sick, frankly, the ignorance and stupidity of

FACT BOX 17

If I sound a little irritable today, it's because I don't feel too well this morning. Well, we all have our ups and downs. The truth is, I met an old friend yesterday. He suggested going to a pub for a drink. I had to explain that I didn't have any cash on me at the moment, but he was exceedingly generous and took me anyway. We drank rather a lot, I'm afraid, and though it was a tremendous night, this morning I do have something of a headache, and feel a little tetchy. I apologise. Though I do believe in honesty: a How To Write writer shouldn't hide what he feels from his readers.

---

some people. I worked as a reader for Crocker & Thistle, in my early days, when I was really desperate for cash and begged them for some work, and the trash I used to have to read. Not that I did read it. I hardly bothered opening the manuscript. They hadn't got a clue. Plonkers, the lot of them. Amateur bloody plonkers who thought they could make lots of money without any effort at all.

I told them. "Rubbish!" I wrote. "Utter garbage." "Should be shredded and thrown into an incinerator." "Don't waste my time, you imbeciles!"

So, it's simple, as the chapter heading says: Study the genre!

'Genre' means 'type of book'. In this case, How To Write Books. Just buy a few, or borrow some from the library, and look at them. See? Easy.

FACT BOX 18

I went back to bed and now feel much better for a few hours' kip, even if the traffic never lets up outside the window. Except I had a dream about the old friend I had a few drinks with last night. In the dream he turned out rather violent towards me, though I have to say he's a really good-natured fellow. I haven't seen him for 20 years. His name's Kurt. I hadn't seen him since his girlfriend, Diane, broke up with him. He's a social worker now, apparently, on secondment from up north, looking after ecstasy-taking joyriding teenagers. I just happened to see him, sitting on his own, in the Indian restaurant, down the road. I wasn't sure it was him at first, well it had been a long time, and he's got a bit stocky now, when he used to be all muscle, and his hair has disappeared from the middle of the top of his head.
He turned out to be a really nice guy, much more interesting and sensitive than I'd guessed all those years ago. I mentioned Diane. He just nodded, so I assumed she was a delicate subject, and I didn't press him.
Amazingly, Kurt had stayed with Lorraine, the nympho I'd

fixed him up with all those years ago. They had five children and were, according to him, though you can never take this sort of thing as gospel, very happy together, though he only gets to go home at weekends. Perhaps they're happy together because he only gets to go home at weekends. It's lucky that I have supreme self-control, not to ask if she was servicing the whole of Bradford, which is where they live. I did tell him that he had me to thank for fixing him up with Lorraine, but that wasn't how he remembered it. He said he had dumped Diane first. Well, I told him, I'm a writer, a How To Write writer, and I've trained my memory, and it's pretty much perfect. In fact, to prove my point, I was tempted to tell him exactly how I'd fixed him up with Lorraine, but I wasn't sure how he'd take that, so I kept quiet.
It was a really good night. We got on so well, chatting about old times, and all the people from those days. I just wish I hadn't had those whiskies on top of all that beer. He was remarkably generous, I must say.
Actually I feel fine now. The hangover's almost completely gone, I'm glad to say. I won't be drinking again for a while, though, I can tell you.

To recap: you'll never be a How To Write writer unless you: *Study the genre!*

chapter seven

Research

Look 'research' up in the dictionary, and you'll find something like: 'investigation, inquiry, looking for information'. And that's what research is. It's looking for information.

I love doing research. So should you, if you've got up and had breakfast and felt that awful weight of depression because you've got yet another blank page to fill, and you're only on page 39 and realistically 150 is the minimum, not including index and opening pages and blurbs. Because that blank paper can stay blank. It's time to do some research!

FACT BOX 19

Interestingly, my dictionary, the Concise Oxford Dictionary, gives the derivation of research as the French 'recherché'. Now 'recherché' means, I believe, something old-fashioned or obscure. What's the connection? Well I shall let you find it out, as a useful exercise. Practice, if you will, in research. [Note to printers: actually, I haven't got a clue, but if I find out before the book's published, I'll change this Fact Box.]

There was a time when I didn't even have to leave the house to do my research, I could switch on the computer, dial up the internet, and there it was, the world library, at the click of a search engine. You can get anything you want on the internet. Of course, things that aren't to do with sex are a little more difficult to find, but they're there, if somewhat more hidden.

These days, since my personal difficulties, I have to go to

the library, as my room doesn't have a phone line, but the use of computers in the library is free, so long as it's not Saturday or the school holidays and booked up with spotty schoolboys looking for wrestling sites or cheats for their stupid computer games.

The most charming feature of the internet is its serendipity. For example, I went to the library yesterday and booked an hour because I needed a list of all the UK publishers of How To Write Books for my appendix.

One hour later, I had found a site devoted to Manchester United-hating football fans, that I could travel to Majorca next week for £17.50 (£43.20 including airport taxes), that an upgrade to Windows Vista (stability guaranteed) was obtainable from eBay for only £139.99, who in the Sopranos will die a horrible death in the next series, that bustybabes.com is blocked by the library server, and that the Golden Lion, my local, does not appear in any good beer guide. That, incidentally, was the only fact that didn't surprise me.

The appendix had to wait for another day, because I was pushed out by some man who was trying to trace the history of his rather mediocre family. But at least I had a reason to go back there, because research never ends, and I had to look at it not as wasting an hour (well, an afternoon, really, if you include waiting for the bus, the setting off to walk when the bus didn't come, only for it to pass as I was in between stops, and calling in at a Costa Coffee shop for a cappuccino and Danish pastry, and browsing the computer magazines in Smiths, wishing I could upgrade the laptop that was given me by a well-meaning friend but is half a second faster than a Remington typewriter). No, I had gained lots of pieces of knowledge that will one day come in useful.

The point I'm making, and it's one often missed by many How To Write writers, is that you don't have to be staring at the computer, or reading stacks of books, or interviewing old people, or visiting various towns, to do research.

Go into a pub and chat to the barmaid, and it's research. Stay at home and play *Civilisation IV* on the computer, and you're doing research. The moment you get up in the morning you're doing research. You can stay in bed all day, sleeping, and that's research. When you've been a How To Write writer as long as I have, every breath of the day is an act of research. Once you're well honed and finely tuned, your very state of being is a state of research, like a Buddhist on the verge of nirvana.

FACT BOX 20

I bumped into Kurt again, as I was coming out of the library. I was really pleased to see him, after that really good night we had in the pub, and was about to suggest we have a quick half in one of the town centre pubs when he gave me a very cold look and walked away without saying anything.

I don't know what's the matter with him. I thought we were getting on like really good mates. I know I didn't buy him a drink, but I did explain my money didn't come in till Thursday. But some people, no matter how much money they have, and I could tell by the credit cards in his wallet he wasn't short of a few bob, just don't like buying a drink when they won't get anything back.

On the other hand, staying in bed most of the day can be rather boring, though I have tried it, especially recently, when I haven't got much money in my pocket and I've got a bit of a cold, and getting up and staring at that bloody screen hour after hour was giving me a tub-thumping headache.

But it needs stating clearly and precisely: research can be whatever you want it to be. Thinking, meditating, getting drunk, watching TV, reading, going on the internet, it's all research for something that one day you may or may not commit to paper.

For example, meeting Kurt again was research. In my story about him and me and Diane, he became a despairing alcoholic, his once muscular body reduced to pulsating flab as he mourned her loss. The only time he got out of his armchair and room was to walk over to the house where Diane and the hero lived, so he could watch from the outside and weep as we bonked in every room, often with the curtains open (that was in the *Mayfair* and not *Woman's Own* version, obviously).

Of course, now he says he was glad that he and Diane split up, but I know that's a justification after the event. He'd still prefer Diane, no matter what he says. But he lost her to me,

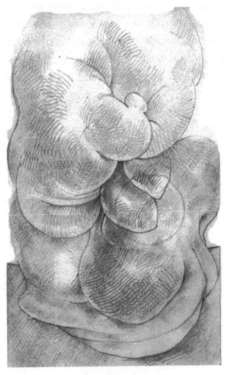

Kurt — a portrait *

* This is Kurt exactly! All stomach, so you don't even know which way up he is. Well done, young Anthony, brilliantly done. You've captured Kurt with precision and truth. Well. In my story, anyway. I suppose really he's still fairly well built and slim.

and now he's suffering so badly he can't face reality. Well, Kurt, you've got to look life squarely in the face sometimes. You can't pretend something didn't happen when it did. As the Americans say: "Get real!"

Lost her to me in the story, I mean. Obviously. And not to me, but to the hero of the story. Although I have to say I do bear more than a little resemblance to him, even if I haven't won Wimbledon.

Actually, now I do know what happened to Kurt it's a lot less interesting than my fiction. In fact it's put me off revising that story, because I was only thinking a few days ago how it would make an excellent film, in the *Four Weddings and a Funeral* or *Love Actually* genre, and might even lead onto the ultimate prize: a *How To Write an English Upper Middle Class Feel-Good Entertainment Screenplay*.

If there is anything to be said for my chatting to Kurt, and this reinforces my point about the serendipitous nature of the researching How To Write writer, it's shown that coincidence is not just a feature of fiction, but does happen in real life. Not a week after I mention the story of Kurt and Diane (see *chapter 3*), there he is, in the town where I live, having a meal at an Indian restaurant. If Stephen King or Dan Brown had told that story you would have quite rightly snorted at their nerve to think you're that credulous. But it happened in real life, and the people who were so scathing over my treatment for a suggested *How To Write the Best Best-Selling Block-Busting Thriller Plots* should eat their humble pork pie hat. Ask Ryan Jinks for the recipe.

The don'ts of research

I'm not a negative person, but after enthusing about research so much, and telling you — and it's true — that whatever you do is fine in the research category, from taking heroin to climbing K2 in your pyjamas, I suppose I should just put in a few cautionary words on the subject. Here are a few things I am convinced you should not do:

1
***Don't** read other How To Write Books.*

It's too depressing. They're so relentlessly cheerful. They fill
you with hope. They suggest that the life of the How To Write
writer is a simple and joyful one of words pouring out of your
brain onto the keyboard, the flow interrupted only by an invitation from your publisher to yet another awards ceremony.

That's the trouble with *The Craft of Writing an Historical
Novel*, by my old pal, Ryan Jinks. It's that tone of: Writing's so
terribly easy. Well, you're dreaming, Ryan.

"Douse yourself in the period of the time you're writing
about by reading as many accounts of the era as you can," he
says.

Frankly, this is dreadful advice. You'll only get confused.
Frankly, and even though historical fiction isn't one of my spe-
cialities (that, and fishing manuals. Oh, and possibly knitting
guides) if you wanted to write a novel about the Romans and
you've watched most of *Gladiator*, I'd say you were as well prepared as you'll ever be. What's Lindsay Davis, or even Tacitus
or Cicero going to add? It's why the Americans are a million
miles ahead of us in the field, at least in terms of sales (and
what else matters?). If Ridley Scott wrote a How To Write Book,
he wouldn't suggest you "Douse yourself in the period". He'd
tell you to find a good looking hero and a first-class special
effects team that can make a wound look manly and get on with
it!

2
***Do** make an exception from number 1 for the truly outstanding How
To Write Books.*

Like **How To Write an Erotic Romantic Short Story**, or **How
To Write a Novel About Modern Working-Class Life**, and of
course the present volume. In fact, if you wanted to write an
historical novel you'll learn more from any of those, or this

book, then from the specious diatribes of *The Craft of Writing an Historical Novel*.

3
***Don't** believe people when they tell you not to play computer games.*

You'll hear this advice a lot: "You're meant to be working, but there you are again, playing that *World of Warcraft/Half Life/SimCity* game."

And of course, frail and unconfident creature that you are, you'll deny it, even if you didn't quite hit the quit button in time as she walked into your study without knocking and there's a sodding great monster on the screen and it's mangling a body with its drooling jaw.

You shouldn't have to deny it. You can work however you want. It's your time. It's your space. It's your life. The proof is in the pudding. If the pudding was tasteless and cold and returned by every publisher in Britain, then it may have been all right for Laura to have said: "It was because you spend too much time playing those games you couldn't get that book published. If you hadn't been playing those games you'd have written a bigger and better book."

Well I'm afraid to say, no, I wouldn't. It's bloody hard being a writer and sometimes you need the relaxation of a game. Who's to say the final work isn't improved by the odd five minutes of *Panzers* or *Total War*?

Laura and I didn't have many arguments in all those years, but this was one of them, and one I still deeply resent. Of course I could have been like Barbara Cartland and produced a book a week or whatever. But what would it have been like? Good products have to be distilled like malt whisky. Take your time. Let its flavour accrue slowly in the oak barrels of your brain. And if that means taking a month to complete all the levels of *Half Life 2*, then if that's what it takes, it takes that, and don't feel guilty.

You can always call it research for writing *How To Write a Computer Game*, though I have to say I found that a hard one to crack. It's a great modern genre, computer games, undervalued, but programmers do seem to know when a new monster should be lurking round the corner or under the floorboards: very frequently. Some of these games will make you change your underpants more than once a day, I can tell you. You really should try them. It's one of the curses of my present situation that I can hardly play solitaire without crashing this crappy laptop that Dan the Van from the pub let me have, because he's a builder and it was superfluous to his needs, as he has to have the most up-to-date and speedy computer there is. For his work. He says. A builder. I ask you.

"It's good enough for word processing," he told me. For processing your words, maybe, I should have said, but not the words of a master professional.

Thanks, Dan, anyway.

4
As far as research is concerned, write your own rules.

You're your own boss. That's what's so great about writing. It's why I gave up teaching. No timetables. No heads of department. No inspections.

You get up when you want, you go to work when you want, you go to the pub or the shops when you want.

Fame and fortune are important, of course, and I've had my share of both. If you ask any honest writer, they'll tell you: "It's the independence, stupid."

That's why we do it.

Some people don't understand, because they're not How To Write writers. Laura didn't, which was a shame.

Not that that was the reason we split up. Not at all. The reasons were many and complex, and I'm sorry, but this book is not the place I intend to go into them!

chapter eight

Structure

I n all the years I spent in How To Write writers' groups, as a Reader for a How To Write publisher, and in discussion with the likes of fellow How To Write writer Ryan Jinks, I never heard more piffle than on the subject of structure and how vital it is.

Ask yourself, what are you doing?

You're writing a book.

You're writing a How To Write Book.

You're not designing the Eiffel Tower. You're not building a skyscraper up from Ground Zero. You're not even making a shed down the bottom of your garden.

It won't fall down. It can't fall down. It's a book, not a house.

If you want to start your How To Write Book with a chapter on 'Dealing with Publishers', masonry will not land on anyone's head. If you finish with 'Choosing a Subject', Health and Safety won't be called in to write a Risk Assessment Policy.

It's up to you. You can put the beginning in the middle, the middle at the end, the end at the beginning, and no deaths will result. The reader might receive a paper cut as he leafs through the book wondering what the hell's going on, but all he'll need is a sticking plaster, not an international disaster relief fund.

You see, I'm a peaceable sort of person, but the one thing that drives me to a fury is someone trying to tell me what I can and can't do.

It's your book. You do what you want. You don't even need to tell the truth, if you really don't want to. For example, I made a slight exaggeration a few pages back when, as an illustration of how coincidences happen in real life, I said that Kurt had appeared in town a couple of days after I'd written about him. In fact I freely admit it was the other way round. He's lived here for about three months, only I'd been avoiding him all this time, assuming he'd want to break my neck after what I did to him with Diane and Lorraine.

FACT BOX 21

Well, the other thing that drives me to a fury is cars and lorries that go at 55 miles an hour along a road that clearly states a speed limit of 30. And when do you ever see a speed cop along here?
Oh, and the other thing that drives me to a fury is speed cameras in some godforsaken village in the middle of Buckinghamshire so you have to pay £40 just before it's your weekend for taking the boys out so you can longer afford the cinema or the zoo or even some Conference League game of footie.

It was only when I saw him wandering round the shopping centre and I followed at a safe distance to check it was really him that I remembered I'd written that story about me and him and Diane. And I fished out that story, and I'll tell you, that story is hot. It certainly arouses me, anyway, and I'm a very cool critic of my own work. No one knows better than I do if I've made a stylistic blemish or grammatically have not quite reached the peak of my usual very high standards.

Frankly, I don't need to be told about structure. The greatest writers have torn up the rule book of their particular genre. Look at James Joyce, and what he did to the novel. Similarly, I feel that I have — if not destroyed — certainly mangled the rule book of How To Write Books.

Of course, you may have the misfortune not to have my technique or experience. Before James Joyce could write *Ulysses* and *Finnegans Wake* he had to do things the traditional way and attempt short stories and straight novels, after all.

So, as a guide, if you can't be bothered to do it yourself and want me to do all the work, here is a suggested list of chapter headings you could use:

Why do you want to be a writer?	*Submitting your idea*
Write what you know	*Publishers and agents*
Choosing your subject	*The world wide web*
Categories	*Self-publishing*
Categories (2)	*Unusual ways of publishing*
Study the genre!	*Redrafting*
Research	*Payment*
Structure	*Translations*
Style	*Bursaries and grants*
Technique	*Awards and festivals*
The title	*Writers' courses*
Your day	*Conclusion*
Writer's block	*FAQs*
Your audience	*Epilogue*
Presentation	*Appendixes*

This happens to be the contents for my first book, but please, have the wit to vary it. Later, when you've got more experience, you'll be able to try something more experimental, become as it were the James Joyce of How To Write writers, as I feel in some small way I have.

In fact my literary career has paralleled his, in many ways. You see, like him, I wrote my early, conventional work, my *Dubliners* and *Portrait of the Artist As a Young Man*, thinly disguised autobiography as a novel. Or in my case, **How To Write a Novel About Modern Working-Class Life** and **How To Write an Erotic Romantic Short Story**.

Once I had proved I could be a success in the conventional field, I, like Joyce, wanted to break the bounds of literary conformism and write the ultimate dream of all How to Write writers:

How To Write A Literary Novel.

Not that I like the phrase, "Literary Novel". What does "Literary" mean? Referring to my trusty Concise Oxford Dictionary, there are two definitions: "1 Using the letters of the alphabet," and I assume that most novels do that, and: "2 Pertaining to literature." In other words, a better way of putting it would be not that we all want to write *How To Write A Literary Novel*, but we want to write:

How To Write a Novel That Will Be Studied at A-level English Literature.

It's not an idle dream. Just think of the volumes of *Lord of the Flies* or *To Kill a Mockingbird* that get shifted because they're on the English Literature GCSE National Curriculum. So just imagine what would happen if Creative Writing was an accredited subject for A-level. What book would be top of the list on the Creative Writing National Curriculum? *How To Write a Novel That Will Be Studied at A-level English Literature*, of course. I've got the notes, and any publisher would snaffle it up, and I could buy a house with the proceeds, even if Laura would thieve her unearned half.

And why shouldn't Creative Writing be studied at A-level? They study Media Studies, and what can you do with a Media Studies A-level? Become the film critic of the Daily Star? Creative Writing — and I would include under that subject the writing of letters, as well as novels (including working-class ones), erotic work, romances, and obviously How To Write Books — is a thousand times more useful than many of today's modern subjects, and a million times more useful than the old ones, like Religious Education or Woodwork.

FACT BOX 22

I spent a long time thinking about writing **How To Write a Novel That Will Be Studied at A-level English Literature**, and concluded that if I could get a publisher interested, then writing it would be a doddle. For instance, just take a look at the first page of Finnegans Wake (and believe me, along with everyone else who's ever looked at it, you won't get any further) and tell me it was difficult to write. Because it's gibberish. You'd think his typewriter finger had got palsy. If you want to reproduce that kind of stuff, then do this: get one of those Voice Recognition Programs for your computer, and put the microphone next to the radio when Woman's Hour is on.

Well, I've done it for you, so try and guess which of these passages is the garbage from a Voice Recognition Program listening to the radio and which is the garbage from Finnegans Wake:

Sample one:
"You could the plane would and of the desert in the medium of the lava in the garden and I head of drivers and noon on. Well animals the ultimate for woozy I mean a year goes into the I'm widely of as you go added a dinner and included in this is that of to the designers."

Sample two:
"Had yet been the and yet at your you room here write incident they wanted 80 looking for the and hear them in what what they are within the week on the year for one of the only fried in setting thoughts at the moment and he is her not to fit at other will the only one at an eye could see the moment that was booked so fit this is booked your satisfaction if this is booked the air."

Go on, then. Guess. I'll put the answer at the end of the chapter, but no peeking before you've thought long and hard about it and had many hours of discussion with your mates down the pub. †
And all right, so James Joyce may not have had a Voice Recognition Program, or even a computer, but my point is that perhaps he was hard of hearing and that's what he

James Joyce at work *

genuinely thought people said. Whatever, it wasn't hard to
write.
Ulysses *isn't* much better. He just wrote down whatever
came into his head. Anyone can do that, if they've got the
nerve. And believe me, that's what the Literary Novel is all
about: having the nerve.

---

* If only I'd been around when Joyce was, and he'd read some of my books, how much
better his novels would have been. I'd have sorted him out, got rid of that self-indulgence,
made sure he had a decent plot in there, and trimmed Ulysses by about 1500 pages.

So, to conclude and recap:

If it's conventional stuff you're after doing then do it conventionally but don't come moaning to me that it's too boring but if it's literary awards you're after then you've got to start thinking in a whole new way and by that I don't mean you're to be original because it's not originality to copy the greats and no one will ever notice anyway because no one will have read the greats and the greats aren't really great they're just cleverer at pretending they're great.

See? James Joyce to a tee. There's nothing to it.

† *Actually, they're both from Voice Recognition Programs listening to Woman's Hour, because I'm not allowed to reproduce any of Finnegans Wake as it's still under copyright. This is obviously and quite fairly to prevent everyone cashing in. As they would. You know, the Hollywood film - "Leonardo DiCaprio is Finnegan in: Finnegans Wake!" - the Finnegans Wake Board Game For All the Family, the Finnegans Wake Stationery Sets, Finnegans Wake alarm clocks ("Finnegans! Wake!"), the whole Finnegans Wake franchise.*

chapter nine

Style

I used to think style was something you either had or you hadn't and you couldn't learn it. You were born with it, or you were born without it, and if you were born with it you had it and if you were born without it you couldn't learn it.

I remember discussing this with Ryan at the launch party for some book of his, published not long after my **How To Write an Erotic Romantic Short Story**. I had dallied for a long time with **How To Write a Novel That Will Be Studied at A-level English Literature**, in one incarnation or another, writing a fairly full synopsis without spending the long hours I knew it would take to write it out.

Unfortunately no publisher was interested, not believing my prediction that Creative Studies would soon be part of the National Curriculum, and I had no money left to publish it myself, so I decided to put it to one side, as one must do with even our greatest potential works, and consider something that would sell, as Laura was six months pregnant with Adam, our first child, and I had given up the part-time contract at school to become a full-time writer.

I considered many subjects, ones that had nagged at me for years with their originality and verve, but none was guaranteed to be published, let alone sell in the kind of quantities I needed if we were to keep our house when Laura would take her maternity leave from the pickle factory.

Finally, one night in the pub, talking to a local journalist, Jack the Hack, it came to me. Well, he suggested it, so that's how it came to me, but once I had put the idea through my How to Write writer's brain, I knew it was what I had been looking for, simple in concept yet bound to be hugely popular:

How To Write a Poem for Your Local Newspaper by **Brian Piddock**. 134 pages. *DL Guppy*. 1999.

This was something I knew a little about, I could research it easily, because I knew where to find Jack — in the Black Horse, from four in the afternoon till 12 at night, usually — and it would be easy to write.

I know what you're thinking. You believe the old saying that a poem is the hardest thing of all to write. You know, when pretentious writers on Radio 4 arts programmes say, "I'd write a poem, but I haven't the time," because they want you to think a poem takes longer to write than a short story, and a short story takes longer than a novel. By that logic, of course, writing a phone book must be the easiest of all.

Well Shakespeare didn't find poetry too difficult, did he? He certainly wrote enough of it, as anyone who's managed to keep awake through *Measure for Measure* on a Wednesday matinee at Stratford will agree.

Let's smash a myth or two here:

Writing poetry isn't difficult.

FACT BOX 23

Laura has always loved Shakespeare's plays. It's not that I don't. I do. I accept that he's part of our heritage. He's a genius. I accept that. I just don't see why I need to go along to any of his plays. People only go to the RSC because they think they ought to be there. They don't want to be there. You'd think you were at a Sleep Laboratory Test if you looked around during a performance at Stratford. Not that I believe the RSC shouldn't be subsidised. I think they should have their subsidy increased, so that they wouldn't need to have an audience. Let them put his works on behind closed doors, then we'll know our heritage is being maintained, and we can do things we want to do and enjoy doing. Needless to say, Laura and I didn't always agree on this, and needless to say she usually won the argument. Bless her.

It's just that poets would like you to think it is. They don't want their freemasonry broken up. And once I'd started the research and read a few poems in our local newspaper I realised why poets and critics despised that kind of work, and called it 'doggerel'. Because it said something. It didn't waffle on about whether you should kill yourself, or the blackness of a crow, or how you should wear the bottoms of your trousers.

They stated, with clarity and purpose:

> *And so the thing you should do*
> *Even if it's at long last*
> *Is build our bloody bypass!*

Or:

> *Fluoride in our water's a sin,*
> *I wouldn't even chuck it in the bin.*

Or:

> *Modern youth,*
> *They're no good.*
> *I'd birch them all,*
> *If I could.*

Simple, effective, and — thank God — they rhymed. And, what was so supremely important as far as I was concerned, written by your ordinary person, not some arty farty ponce with pretensions to literary greatness.

In other words, there was a big, big audience.

I have to say that **How To Write a Poem for Your Local Newspaper** proved me right in every way. It sold 112 copies in the first month alone. And if it increased the number of people who write letters of complaint in verse to their newspaper, that's a bonus, and one I'm very proud of.

This wasn't, though, how Ryan saw it.

Perhaps you've heard of Ryan Jinks. Perhaps you've even

read some of his books. They're quite enjoyable, in their own little way. But even his best friends — and naturally I include myself in that list — would never say that his writing is stylistically elegant.

FACT BOX 24

I don't want to give the impression that all local newspaper poems are complaining. I still fondly remember the poem sent to me by Mrs Allington, a lady who lived in Chester. The poem was, she said, inspired by my book:

It was back in 1932
That I first visited our zoo.
It was a lovely place then
With Jim the lion and a rhino called Ben.

And finishing, forty-two verses later:

Of course those times, they've all gone.
To wish them back is forlorn
Today's young folk have got it made
They scarcely know that they've been born.

In fact once or twice I've had to point out to him some errors. His punctuation (whole chapters can go by without a single exclamation mark — so necessary for lightening his rather sticky prose) and his incorrect use of fonts (*italics* are so important, as are **bold** or <u>underlining</u> for stressing what needs to be stressed — otherwise how can the pressed-for-time reader skim a page?). The lack of clarity this produces. But I always mentioned these points in the spirit of helpfulness. How can you go on to be a better writer unless you listen to and take note of your friends, especially those with more experience and ability than yourself?

I suspect, though, that he took my advice in the wrong way,

and had been jealously waiting several years before he could get, as he might put it, his own back.

You see, one of my contributions to the How To Write Book field, my own personal style, has to do with the occasional anecdote. Just a little story here or there helps to leaven what otherwise might be pages of dull instruction. Anecdotes are the colour of a How To Write Book. They are the picture, the vibrancy, absolutely necessary, I believe, to the well-rounded How To Write Book.

Unfortunately, Ryan goes, I believe, too far.

Not long after he moved to this town, and when he discovered that I was an established author, he asked me if I'd have a look at his first How To Write work, *Writing Dragon-Flying Fantasies*, and gave me the manuscript on a floppy disk.

I did a word search on the word "I", whole word, match case. It came up with 132 instances. In a 97 page book! This, I'm afraid, is not leavening instruction with anecdotes, it's pure egotism.

If I have a fault, it's honesty, and at that launch of Ryan's latest opus, I felt compelled to point out this fault. There were, I remember, a few people there, in the Bear Arms function room, hired by Ryan for the purpose of flogging his book to his mates. He came over to chat.

Ryan has a beard and moustache. It covers most of his face, it seems, so it's difficult to see what expression he has, though I believe he was smiling at that moment, as of course he had every right, his book being published, his friends helping him to celebrate.

So I thought, if he's in a good mood, this would be the moment to gently put it to him that he ought to increase the advice-to-personal-anecdote ratio, and I said something to the effect that I hoped this new effort of his wasn't all about him again.

Well I'm afraid I believe that Ryan must have been one of those boys at school, and I've come across quite a few in my time, who will never admit they don't know everything, and this is not a useful attribute when you're learning calculus, or

The beard of Ryan Jinks *

indeed trying to succeed in the often cut-throat How To Write world.

He caused quite a stir. I knew he had a temper, I'd seen him physically attack someone once in the White Lion when the bloke had only made a passing comment about black people. But I never expected the diatribe I received that evening, the gist of it coming down to a juvenile sort of: "You stink more than me," as far as I could tell, under the flowery fury.

I laughed it off. You have to really. You have to be confident that your work is good and secure in history, and I'm afraid

---

* *This is obviously just a beard. Anthony Connolly hasn't actually bothered to go and find Ryan and draw him. Not that I blame him for that, he'd probably be regaled with the never ending stories of Ryan's prowess, as all of us have at one time or another.*

that Ryan showed he doesn't feel that about his work.

I looked, later, at the work he was launching that evening, *The Craft of Writing the TV Makeover Follow-Up Book* (Laura had bought a copy). The very first sentence began with "I". I thought, no wonder he's so sensitive, poor dear.

The point I want to make is that there are two styles appropriate to How To Write Books. There is a typical style of the run-of-the-mill How To Write writer, full of self-publicity, boasting of the author's abilities, practically adverts for their books, including price, publisher, and year of first edition.

Or, it is possible to show a little restraint. Obviously you sometimes must give the reader a reason to do something, and that reason will probably come from personal experience. But I believe you can overdo that kind of thing. You're not writing How I Wrote It, are you?

By the way, that incident between Ryan and myself didn't cause any kind of rift in our friendship. I think we're both bigger than that. Well I'm certainly a few inches taller than him, and I've beaten him at squash a few times! No, we never referred to his outburst, and I think that was the right reaction. How To Write writers can be over-sensitive. After all, they see themselves as the teachers, and, if you remember, teachers at school often resented being corrected, as much by their superiors as pupils.

I hope that you, the budding How To Write writer, will not have such a delicate ego.

In summary:

1   Variation is useful.
2   Grammar, please.
3   Spelling: beware American spell checkers.
4   Punctuation: beware the exclamation mark! †

---

†   *I put that one there in an ironical way!* ‡
‡   *(and that one)!*

chapter ten

Technique

The How To Write writer should have many weapons in his armoury to use in the writing of his How To Write Book. Here are some of them:

1   **Humour**

2   **Suspense**

There are others, and I'll come to them soon, if this traffic would only pause for half a minute. It's the lorries that are the worst. The whole building vibrates. The thing is, I've got to go out at 12 to see about getting a job at the local betting shop. They pay £6.25 an hour, which is frankly an insult for someone with my qualifications, but when you're desperate you'll take anything. Such is the life of the How To Write writer.

1   Humour

I don't mean tell a few jokes. I don't see the point of jokes in a How To Write Book. In one of Ryan's volumes he told a joke about a man and a canary going into a pub. You've probably heard it. I think everyone's heard it. They meet a penguin, and the bartender's deaf. It's not very good, although I'm sure after five pints in the pub you might get a few titters.

I don't mean tell jokes. Unless, of course, you're writing: **How To Write a Good Joke**. And then you could just look at a dozen joke books and select a hundred or so. Actually, that's not a bad idea. Remember, I thought of it first. I'll have to mention it to the good folk of my present publishing house before they print this one and all you thieving bastards nick the idea!

Now that last sentence was more what I mean about humour. Not a joke, but something stated in a lighter vein, and guaranteed to raise a smile (though I meant it about **How To Write a Good Joke** being my idea, so don't even think about it).

You need to let your reader know that writing a How To Write Book is not a grim affair. It may be solitary. There may be days of absolute bloody torture when not a word occurs to you, and you think about overdosing on sleeping pills (if you've got any, and believe me if you lived where I'm living, and the traffic only stopped between 3.45 and 3.50am, you'd have a good stock) because you just can't take the pain of realising that all your dreams of becoming a great and respected writer are nothing but the delusions of youth, and why didn't you become a merchant banker like your old mate Wes (who was frankly less intelligent and far worse educated than you) and have holidays in the Maldives and an apartment in Dubai and a bank account with more noughts than the age of the universe, and you can't even have an uninterrupted day because society is too pig ignorant to allow its artists the few pennies they need to live and you have to go and demean yourself by trying to get a stupid job in a stupid betting office.

But occasionally, you'll find a moment when you can smile. And it's important to remember that, especially at black times.

2   Suspense

This is another technique the How To Write writer can use to keep the reader going through what might otherwise be a rather dull and didactic work. Don't tell them everything at the beginning of the chapter. Let them discover the secrets slowly.

Here's an example of something suspenseful that happened to me just a few minutes ago, as I was on my way back here from the betting shop, and will prove useful, I think, as an illustration of what I mean. I didn't get the job, by the way. They gave it to a 19-year-old. I was naturally rather despondent about this, and was wondering if I might have enough cash for a pint in the pub when I saw Kurt, in the street.

I'd assumed that he'd been avoiding me because, although I had no recollection of it, I wondered if I'd told him, under the benign influence of a few pints of beer, about how I'd set him up with Lorraine all those years ago so that he'd split up with Diane.

Diane. Or Lorraine *

I couldn't have been more wrong. I had, apparently, told him, but he didn't mind that at all. It was, after all, a long time ago, he said, and since he was now married to Lorraine he was grateful to me. No, he said, if he'd not sought me out it was only that he didn't want me to feel embarrassed that I hadn't enough money to buy a round.

I told him I wasn't embarrassed at all. I've worked hard all my life. I'm still working hard, and if financially things have not panned out as they might have done then that's bad luck and not slothfulness.

He understood. I do think he's a really decent fellow, and I wish I'd known him better at university.

Then, as we stood chatting, in the pedestrianised area just outside Marks & Spencers, he told me this quite amazing thing:

He knows where Diane lives.

More than that, staggeringly more, he's been in touch with her recently, mentioned me to her, and she admitted that for all this time since university she had been desperate to see me — this is 22 years! — because she always loved me but could never tell me. Absolutely astounding. I don't know why she couldn't have told me. Fear of rejection, I suppose, though — silly girl! — I'd never have rejected her.

She lives in Edinburgh now, apparently, which is a hell of a long way away. I asked Kurt for her phone number, but he said that for some reason, afraid of being stalked or something, she can only take certain incoming calls. What he suggested is that Diane and I meet. That was what she wanted. I can hardly believe it, it was all so sudden and unexpected, especially after I'd only just been thinking about her, and how much I wished we'd got together, and me telling Kurt all this, and then he springs this on me.

You see what I mean about coincidence? You wouldn't believe it if it was fiction.

The only trouble is, she can't travel down here to see me. Something about long journeys. And I haven't the cash to get up to Edinburgh. That's another reason I need a job, apart from the Social Security telling me. It costs £94.10 return to go to Edinburgh! Well, I could just get a single, at £75.50. What have I got here to keep me here? The boys would miss their weekends with me, obviously, and I've got a lot of very good friends, but sometimes it's good to make a clean break.

I just never realised. All that time, gone, wasted, oh the pity of it. Though it makes it all somehow more poignant.

So here's a very good example of the use of suspense. I've arranged to see Kurt again tomorrow, as he had to dash off, so you, like me, will have to wait to find out what happens between Diane and me. I wonder how much she's changed. Kurt says she's as lovely as ever. This seems to me so like Fate.

3   Conflict

That's another useful tool the How To Write writer should use. After all, it is ever present in the How To Write writer's life, in his or her battles with publishers, agents, critics, even readers. Not to mention landlords, bank managers, electricity companies, so-called friends, publicans, youths in the street, traffic wardens, and council officials.

For example, in discussing techniques, you could mention that one How To Write writer believes in giving long-winded and overprecise instructions, while another is more easy-going and allows the putative How To Write writer to develop his own technique. Then leave it to the reader to decide which is best, preferably without weighting the argument to one side or the other.

4   The Chapter Hook

I'd forgotten this one, even though it's one of my personal contributions to the features of How To Write Books. It means ending a chapter at a point when not everything has been resolved, so the reader is desperate to turn to the next chapter.

For instance, if you look back at chapter 9, '**Style**', I didn't say everything that could be said on the subject, but left a few points in this chapter, so you couldn't put the book down and had to keep on reading, even though it was nearly midnight and you have to be up early tomorrow.

The Chapter Hook is like the old Music Hall saying: "Leave them wanting more". It means not crossing all the t's and dotting the i's. When the reader reaches the end of the chapter he isn't sated by information. On the contrary, he is keen to get more.

FACT BOX 25

There was a good example of conflict in the betting shop after that interview. I felt like smashing the manager's teeth in, and I'm not a violent sort, but there was a moral principle here. A 19-year-old. I told the manager it was ageism. He claimed it was because of my past, and that I hadn't mentioned it on the application. As if you have to put every little detail on an application to work in a betting shop! It's an immoral occupation, anyway, taking money from gamblers. It's preying on the weak and the addicted and should be banned.

But in a sense something good has come out of that, because I've just seen Kurt again, in the Star and Garter, his local, and when I told him I wouldn't have the money to go to Edinburgh, and couldn't he get her to contact me somehow, or better still ask her to make the trip down here, he said, and I thank God I met him after all these years, that he'd buy me the train ticket!

I was staggered that he'd do this for me. He really is the most generous person I've met.

---

5   Register

The register is the voice you use in your work. It's your voice. Don't imitate anyone else's. Don't let anyone tell you it's not a nice voice. If you're excited, then that's fine, because why shouldn't you be excited, so excited you can't sleep and you don't want the reader to sleep, you keep thinking of new ideas and new subjects and Edinburgh! — and you want it all to burst out of you.

Speak how you want. That's what I believe. Say what you want to say as loudly as you want. Even if you can hardly believe the way that life goes, just when you think you're at your lowest point, suddenly it's all just marvellous. Don't even think about those 22 years. They're not wasted. They were a preparation for this moment.

I can't wait!

chapter eleven

The title

I've touched on this in chapters 1, 2, 3, 4, 5, 6, 8, and 9, but it will do no harm to reiterate the point:

The title is the most important part of your How To Write Book!

Put yourself in the place of your potential reader. He or she has recently noticed that there's an awful lot of biographies about people who had terrible childhoods, almost as many as there are biographies by or about Wayne Rooney or Princess Di, and they're sitting on that table in Waterstones that suggests they're as popular.

You know the sort of thing I mean:

My Stolen Childhood.

The Boy with No Trousers.

A Troubled Girl.

People love this kind of thing. Maybe it makes them feel better, that someone else feels worse.

So your canny reader thinks:

"My childhood wasn't great. After all, I had a brother and a sister, so I didn't get all the attention from my father and mother. I lived opposite someone whose dad was a merchant banker, so he always got better Christmas presents than me. We only had a Ford Fiesta, and all my friends laughed when I was picked up from school.

"Frankly, it's a wonder I grew up as well-balanced as I have.

"I'd like to tell my deprived story. But where do I start? What do I include? How do I sell my manuscript?"

They need you, the How To Write writer, to answer all their questions. But how are they going to find you? They go into Smith's or Waterstones, and they say to the gormless lad behind the desk:

"I want to write a book like one of those," and they point at the pile.

"You want to write Wayne Rooney's autobiography?" the gormless lad says.

"No!" They go over, and show him a copy of *Never Had Nothing*. "This book."

So what's the gormless lad going to do? Spend an hour looking fruitlessly on his computer screen for a How To Write Book about Never Had Nothing, until he decides to ask his supervisor, who, aware that there are people with cash in their hand waiting to be served, swiftly weighs up the time spent investigating obscure book versus ready money dropping into the till, tells Mr or Mrs Reader that no such book has ever been or ever will be published.

So the reader goes home, or to the library (if there's a space amongst the computers from spotty wrestling-fixated schoolboys), gets onto Amazon, and types in: '*How To Write*'.

1584 results.

Advanced search: '*kids*'.

0 relevant results.

Advanced search: '*troubled*'.

0 relevant results.

Ditto '*childhood*', '*stolen*', and '*heartbreaking*'.

And your potential reader, now your erstwhile potential reader, decides that it's true, there is no How To Write Book about deprived childhoods.

All because you called your work:

How To Write a Book about Your Deprived Youth.

Well, you thought long and hard, and discussed this with your publishers, and agreed you had to be specific. But how specific? You thought of '*Deprived Childhood*', but that might miss all those people whose teenage life was deprived. You wanted to include all ages, from 0 to 19. So you went for '*Deprived Youth*', because, frankly, you were greedy.

If you'd just thought for a moment you could have written

two books, virtually identical, *How To Write a Book about Your Deprived Childhood* and *How To Write a Book about Your Deprived Teens*. Or even a series, *How To Write a Book about Your Deprived Babyhood, How To Write a Book about Your Deprived Infancy, How To Write a Book about Your Deprived Preteens, How To Write a Book about Your Deprived Adolescence*, and so on.

FACT BOX 26

Misery Memoirs, these books are known as, to people in the trade. So why didn't you write How To Write a Misery Memoir? Well, because the term Misery Memoir is rather derogatory, and ironic, and postmodern, and people writing Misery Memoirs don't want to be that, do they? You can't be miserable as well as derogatory and ironic and postmodern, can you? Just try it, and you'll see what I mean.

After all, this is a rich field. I've often thought about writing these myself, but to do so would mean thinking back to my own childhood, and frankly I believe the experience would be too painful. In fact thinking about it even now makes me break out into a cold sweat, I get palpitations, and I feel tears well up in my eyes.

You see, and it takes an enormous amount of courage for me to write these words, but neither of my parents hit me. They never forgot my birthday or Christmas. They talked to me. They took me on holiday. I had friends at school. I can't remember getting into a single fight. I had a great train set, I used to play with it a lot, when I wasn't reading all the books I was provided with.

Which is why I resent Mum and Dad so much, because there's not enough there for a pamphlet, let alone a book. They deprived me of my deprived childhood, and for that I can't forgive them.

Well, I do, because they're all right, fuss a bit, and ring me at least once a week, and I wish they had bigger pensions so they could loan me the odd fifty quid, but I still get a good meal if I go home.

I wish I had a house as nice as theirs, too, in the suburbs. And I wish I had been as lucky as he was, a bank manager who retired when he was 50, with enough redundancy money to buy a little apartment in the Algarve. Mum always says how proud she is to see my name on the cover of my books. They have a shelf put aside, just for my works. Not the whole of the shelf, of course, but a decent part of it (especially since it includes 10 copies of *How To Write an Erotic Romantic Short Story*).

FACT BOX 27

Though I do deplore the habit of some publishers who omit the name of the author on the spine of some How To Write books. Especially since I discovered on that shelf in Mum and Dad's house one of the books, next to mine, was Writing Dragon-Flying Fantasies. I put that in the bin sharpish, I can tell you.

So the title is paramount. Put yourself in the mind of the average, and therefore not too bright, potential writer. He or she is not a professional, or they wouldn't need your advice. They have no idea how the book trade works. They hardly read any books, but they watch telly, and they say to their spouses after an episode of *Silent Witness* or *The Bill*: "I've got a better idea than that." Or: " I could have thought of a better twist at the end." Or: "I would have had her do it, not him."

And you can bet your last fiver the spouse will say, "Why don't you, then?"

"What?"

"Write a better one!"

And he, goaded by his wife's sarcastic lack of faith in him, says:

"I will!"

They don't mean it, of course. Especially not for TV, which they assume is run by a clique whose entry is only permitted by those who went to the right school and university. They assume quite rightly, incidentally, as I can vouch, having submitted my own idea, together with two of my books, to the Head of Features at the BBC, ITV, Channel 4 and Five. It's a brilliant idea, too. I thought, initially, of a series on BBC2 or Channel 4, at around 8pm. I'd have done the presenting, the Simon Schama of the How To Write world. I've often been told down the pub that I have the voice and manner of a TV presenter.

My suggested title was, *So You Want to Be a Writer?* which I think has the zip and go required for TV. The initial run was to be six parts, covering the obvious genres — thrillers, historical novels, science fiction, bonkbusters, and so on — and after that had done well, a second run of the second string subjects, and, who knows, a third and fourth series.

They didn't even write me a letter. Just a slip of paper stating that the schedules were full at the moment, and if I wanted my books returned could I send the postage.

Pig ignorant, those TV controllers. They wouldn't know a good idea if it jumped off the pavement and slapped them about the face. I tell you, the audience potential is huge. But no, they'd rather have their petty quiz shows and cod history programmes and so-called reality TV.

So Mr or Mrs Joe Public immediately assume TV is not for them, it's controlled by extraterrestrial beings, and they have a point. Books, on the other hand, they believe, are quite a different matter, perfectly democratic and open to the most amateurish scribbler. They think, "Well, Wayne Rooney's had a book published, I'm brighter than Wayne Rooney, I can have a book published." Of course, logically, this is what is known as a syllogism. As in:

All hippos are grey, my dishwasher is grey, therefore my dishwasher is a hippo.

Yes, Wayne Rooney has had a book published. Yes, they are brighter than Wayne Rooney. But no, they cannot get a book published because they are not one of the most famous British people alive. You want to have a book published? My advice: become an international footballer. Or read the news on TV. Or appear on *Big Brother*. That's the fast route for today's author.

But Joe doesn't know this. He needs help. He probably hasn't got any paper. He probably hasn't got a pen. He needs fairly basic assistance, and you are there to take his £11.99 off him to do him a good turn.

So how does he find you? There has to be a word he is thinking of that's the word you've got in your title. Put yourself into his mind — this is the job of the How To Write writer, to be empathetic. Does he think, "I want to write a book about my deprived childhood?" He may. Or it may be that deprived has two too many syllables. Bad childhood would be the answer, except *bad* is the kind of word the search engine would ignore or return several million hits. *Poor* is better. Everyone thinks they're childhood was poor. Prince Charles and Paul Getty 15th think their childhood was poor. It's all a matter of perspective.

Even so, *poor* isn't going to be much better as a search word. So you've rejected *deprived, bad, poor,* and you still haven't found the perfect word. But it's there, you know it is. So what do you do, to find this perfect word that is so vital, the difference between success and failure?

I don't know. I have to leave something for you to do. I can't be wiping your bottom still. You're a grown adult, and you have to take responsibility for something.

I simply stress: *Titles Are Important.*

I remember discussing this with Ryan, on one of the last times we spoke civilly to each other. He'd asked me what I'd thought about his book. This was about three months after the launch he had in the Bear Arms, and of course I hadn't had the chance to read it. I mean I'm with Oscar Wilde on this one, if I want to read a good How To Write Book, I write it first. I'd glanced in the index and bibliography of his book to see if my name was mentioned, and of course, Ryan being rather a jealous sort of chap, only two of my books were there.

But I thought about the title: *The Craft of Writing About Your Terminal Illness.* Now I'm by no means old-fashioned or conventional, anyone who knows me will agree that I'm a most adventurous person, to a fault, or I probably wouldn't have ended up in this pokey little bedsit beside one of the busiest arterial roads in the universe. But a How To Write Book cannot, by definition, not have How To Write in the title. How To Write tells you what it is. It's simple. It's direct. It's essential. And certainly it's better than using an arty farty airy fairy word like '*craft*'. You're not doing woodwork, or making a model aeroplane! You're putting words down on a piece of paper. Or hard disk. There's no craft to it. You're born with language. Or learn it fairly quickly. If you can speak, you can write. That's what I believe.

The trade of the How To Write writer consists of pointing out those less obvious but important features of a book, how to write an effective subheading, when to use bold and when italics, who to send your book to. Frankly, the word '*craft*' makes me want to puke. It sounds Germanic, and I'm not keen on the Germans, and I'm not just talking about football here, I'm talking about that school trip to Bavaria, when I liked that girl Frieda and she got off with Jeff Plumley. I mean, Jeff Plumley!

If you remember nothing else from this book, if you do nothing that it advises except one: *Please, please, use **How To Write** in your title*.

No.

I'm not even going that far. Use what you want in the title, *Handbook of... A Course in... Writing for...*

But not, ever, *The Craft of...*

If you do, you can send this book back to me and I shall refund your money. If you're that stupid you don't deserve to possess this work (actually, my publishers tell me that it would be advisable not to make that a binding pledge, so I make it binding only in a metaphorical sense).

Naturally, I couldn't tell Ryan what I thought of his book. I'd already seen what a sensitive little flower he was after any hint of criticism or advice.

So I said:

"It was very interesting."

FACT BOX 28

  "In a metaphorical sense" *is, by the way, a most useful expression, and will save you many visits to the libel court. Say, for example, you want to mention in your book that your former next-door neighbour is a fat, lying, bald, dishonest creep, because he went on and on about that branch on your apple tree that leaned over into his garden until finally it blew down and broke his fence and he started shouting at you (yes, Mr Stacey, that's you). So you call him a fat, lying, bald, dishonest creep. Fine. Except you might get sued for a lot of money.*

No problem. To avoid a writ, just say: "Of course, I mean that metaphorically."

And with one bound, you're free! No court in the land could find for the plaintiff.

That advice alone is worth the purchase price of this book.

I would recommend this as a catchall phrase for any situation where a writer asks you what you think about his work. If you've read, or not read the book. If you don't like it, or you hate it. Don't offend the poor chap or chappess. Just say:

"It was very interesting."

And you've retained your dignity without being hypocritical. You could have meant, in fact you did mean: "It was very interesting to discover that you were capable of writing such utter balderdash." Or: "It was very interesting that your book wasn't quite as bad as I expected, in that you got the page numbers in the right order."

And he or she won't be offended. They think you mean the subject matter, the fluent way they expressed it, are of exceeding interest. Because they are, frankly, arrogant sods.

If, however, they are so delicate and insecure that this isn't enough for them, and I could see the doubt in Ryan's expression, as much as you can see any expression with that bloody beard that hides his probably exceedingly weak chin, there is a follow up expression that will smooth away any ill feeling.

"No, it was certainly very interesting," I repeated. And I added (wait for it):

"Well done."

Of course, I meant well done for being such a jammy bastard as to get this pile of crap accepted by a publisher who obviously hadn't learned to read, but let me assure you "Well done" sounds to a writer like an award, and he or she will hear it and see themselves on the stage, Booker Prize cheque in their hand, about to make their acceptance speech.

"Thank you," said Ryan. "I feel it's my best one yet."

You have to note the 'yet'. It's absolutely bloody brilliant, he's telling me, but he can do better, because he is a genius, him. If Shakespeare were still around he'd be grovelling at Ryan's feet in admiration.

FACT BOX 29

There is a third phrase to use to authors if you can't even bring yourself to say, "It was interesting," or "Well done," because you detest their work but lack the heart to crush them totally. Which is:

"You must be very pleased."

This is only to be used when you consider the work to be so dreadful the flames that burn it would die of shame.

And remember, you writers, if anyone says to you, when they read your work:

"You must be very pleased."

You may as well go home and take a large dose of tablets, because you've just been given the Phrase of Death.

It's almost a duty, I feel, not to let this kind of arrogance pass. Ryan is not a genius. He could only dream of striving towards mediocrity. I had to enter some note of criticism, just to bring him back to earth, it was for his own good, or he'd be taking to wearing doublet and hose and saying, "Forsooth".

And since I had only read the bibliography, or only that part that mentioned my books, and everything was spelt correctly, I could only talk about the title, which luckily was, as I said, execrable.

"Not sure about the title, though," I said.

This was probably a mistake. I should know not to upset Ryan's feelings, or you won't hear the end of it. We had a bit of an argy bargy, with him revealing his extraordinary prejudices, such as not liking the use of *How To Write* in the title, amazingly enough. I suppose that says it all about him, really.

The thing about Ryan, I always find it difficult to talk to him because of that stupid little earring he wears in his left ear. As he talks it judders. I find I'm not looking at his eyes, which are anyway rather small and close set, but staring at that bit of swinging metal attached to his left ear.

Anyway sometime during this discussion we got onto which was the better title: **How To Write a High Concept Science-Fiction Novel** or *The Craft of Writing A High Concept Science-Fiction Novel*.

Now, he has since claimed that he mentioned High Concept Science-Fiction before I did. He says that I didn't even know what High Concept Science-Fiction was before I talked to him. This is nonsense. I don't know where I heard of it, but I know it wouldn't have been from him.

The point I was trying to make was that *The Craft of Writing A High Concept Science-Fiction Novel* was not only dreadfully long winded, and wouldn't hit the target audience, but 'craft' and 'high concept' belonged to two worlds several thousand light years away from each other.

"All right," he said, "as an alternative, what's wrong with *Writing a High Concept Science-Fiction Novel*?"

"Because it's describing what you're doing, not what you want to say, which is how to do it," I stated.

I don't believe we reached an agreement, but I do know that later that night it occurred to me that I'd written at least one High Concept Science-Fiction story. Plus I'd had several ideas for some High Concept Science-Fiction stories. That

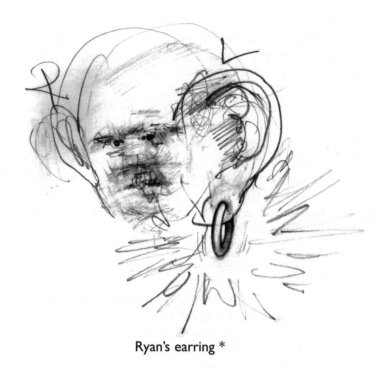

Ryan's earring *

could be my next work. And I set out on the long process of planning and researching: **How To Write a High Concept Science-Fiction Novel**.

Then, of course, I hear that Ryan is about to publish *The Craft of Writing A High Concept Science-Fiction Novel*, and when I approach him, outraged that he has stolen my idea, he claims that that night he had told me he had started his book. But I know that would have registered, despite his bloody pretentious earring. I'm quite sure that I used it in our discussion on titles as an example, plucked out of my fertile brain like so many of my ideas, and he decided that wasn't a bad idea.

* * *

* Yes, all right, thank you, Connolly, that's enough of Ryan. It's an earring. We can all imagine an earring. We don't want to imagine Ryan. Even if I do, despite myself. And that bit of metal. The way it goes jingle jangle. Jingle jangle. Silently.

My advice: Keep your ideas to yourself. It's a dog-eat-dog world, the How To Write Books world, and you've only yourself to blame if you generously chat to someone in an open and trusting way, never dreaming they'll turn out to be a plagiarising rat.

It's moments like that, when Ryan announced his new book was finished and about to be published, and I casually asked him what it was called, and he told me, and I thought of all the time I'd spent in researching my own work on High Concept Science-Fiction, and all the notes I'd made, and my chapter list, that strike you with the force of an epiphany. If epiphanies have force. I suppose they're rather ineffable things. Life changing, anyway. A moment you'll never forget.

FACT BOX 30

I had one of those Life Changing Epiphanies last week. It's worth mentioning because they're so important in the development of the How to Write writer. It happened when I went to Edinburgh to see a girl, Diane, from university. A Life Changing Epiphany is the only way to describe it.

By the way, if you're not in the trade you may not understand what High Concept Science-Fiction is. I can best describe it by giving an example of a High Concept Science-Fiction novel I had a great idea for, though I didn't quite get round to writing it.

It was all about gravity stopping.

One day the hero is walking down the street and he gets on a bus, and gravity as a force suddenly ceases to exist, and the bus floats away into the sky, and he floats in the bus, until he is up the sky and looking down on a disintegrating world.

Actually, he probably wouldn't be the hero because he'd be dead within a few minutes, as the atmosphere got lost. And I wasn't quite sure of the technical reason why gravity should stop suddenly. Perhaps a weapon some aliens had developed.

Or more likely an allegory for how we take things for granted, like gravity, and how they can cease at any moment. Although science-fiction isn't very keen on allegories. And it probably isn't very high concept, because high concept has to be big, a whole different view of the universe, a different universe, different form of life, so that idea isn't a great example. More like an example of low concept science-fiction.

Or, here's a better example, another idea I had: electricity, for some reason, stops working. Maybe the magnetic poles switch, north to south and south to north, and while they do, electricity goes haywire. I don't know if that would happen. I'll have to check it out, if I ever write that story. But the effect is easy to imagine: no cookers (unless they're gas), or lighting (except for candles), or computers, or communications. The world would enter a period of darkness, both literally and symbolically, though literally is more important in the High Concept Science-Fiction novel.

Actually, even that idea is rather parochial and low concept, because you'd have to centre on the hero or heroine who lived in the city, and their desperate attempts to flee the rioting mob. A bit like *The Day of the Triffids*, without the triffids.

2001: A Space Odyssey. That's a High Concept Science-Fiction idea. In fact it's so high concept no one has a clue what it's about. Which is probably the definition of High Concept Science-Fiction. It's science-fiction if James Joyce had written it.

Yes, I'm quite glad I never got round to writing **How To Write A High Concept Science-Fiction Novel**, because there's hardly any decent examples, and no one really knows what it means. I notice that Ryan's final title was *Writing a Big Science-Fiction Novel*, which is probably the feeblest title I've ever heard. What was wrong with *Writing a Rather Longer Than Average Science-Fiction Novel*, Ryan? I can't think of any other How To Write writer who would so lack self-respect they'd use 'Big' in their title. I hope no one reading this book ever does anything so miserable. How his publishers allowed it, I'll never know, but then they're hardly in the top flight of How To Write Book publishers (unlike the publishers of this book!). I was quite glad I had given Ryan the idea, and abandoned it myself, if that was the humiliating result. I can't imagine the sales figures. At least the book will help in the widening of the M25. I believe that's what happens to unsaleable books, they get pulped into the tarmac. That's a nice thought, the next time I drive down the motorway, when I get my licence back, that Ryan is performing a useful service for once, softening the thud of my tyres.

Titles are important:
Get them right and you've got it made!

chapter twelve

Your day

This is My Day:
I get up at 6.30am, go for a four-mile run, shower, have a light breakfast, and sit down to work by 7.30. I write solidly for the next two and a half hours, have an espresso and do the Times crossword, and return to the laptop by 10.30, and don't pause again until after 1pm. After a light lunch I spend the afternoon correcting the morning's work, and then I turn to lighter matters, writing my columns for the national newspapers and the New Statesman, ringing my publisher or agent. The evenings are usually taken up with an awards ceremony, or dinner with a fellow writer or a media executive. After Ovaltine at midnight, and a chapter of *Middlemarch*, I'm asleep by 12.30.

That's the kind of stuff you'll read in the Sunday colour supplements, *A Day in the Life* of Ian McEwan or Graham Swift. Ignore it. It's lies. You know why they say it? To make the rest of us feel bad. So bad we don't have the nerve to type another word. It eliminates the competition by making them feel so inadequate they'll never write again.

Don't listen to them.

The writer's average day goes something like this:

The traffic wakes me at 7. I stay in bed till 8. I'd like to sleep on, but it's impossible with Eddie Stobart's men trying to demolish every building in the street. I go for a two-mile walk, to get a newspaper. The nearest newsagent is 100 yards away, and the next nearest half a mile, but I don't go in either of them, on principle, because they claim I haven't paid my bills with them.

I don't bother with breakfast, unless there's a piece of bread in the cupboard. I have several cups of coffee, until I'm awake enough to switch on the laptop, usually at about 11.15. The laptop, which is probably the only steam-driven computer in existence (thank you, Dan the Van), is ready for use at 11.40. I play a quick game of *Warcraft 3*, but the processor's so slow I get killed three times by 11.55, so I play solitaire for the next hour.

At 1, I have lunch, if I've got any food in the place. If not, I'll go out, and see if there's anyone I know down the pub.

At 3, I'll return to the laptop, and start work in earnest. If I've done a particularly good paragraph, I'll go and have a lie down.

At 5, I'll go to the library to check my e-mails. Afterwards, it's not worth going home, so I go down the pub and see my mates.

At 12, on average, I'll get back to my room and sleep.

Not quite the same as McEwan or Swift. But does it matter? Of course not! The quality of the work is what's important, and I defy anyone to tell which page was written when I had a raging hangover and it took me a week of agony, and which rolled onto the screen as if dictated directly by some spooky outside agency.

Can you tell, looking at that paragraph above, whether it was god-given or wrought through torture? Of course you can't! To you, every word of mine is a precious jewel. And so it must be when *you* work, even if you can't match my priceless prose.

If you want to get up at midday, that's your privilege. If you want to spend all the opening hours God and the government's given you in the pub, then, as the Australians say, don't beat yourself up over it.

In fact, I have to admire your discipline, because if I ever have a day when I do no writing at all I always feel guilt, as if there really is a God, and he or she is saying: "Tut tut, Brian, that's another day gone by, you're 45, or so, and you still haven't written that Great Book that I know is in you."

Of course it's different when you do something unusual and positive in the day. That's reaping experiences and doing research. Like Tuesday, when I took a whole day off and went up to Edinburgh. It's a long way to Edinburgh. I hadn't realised, and I had to change trains twice, once at Birmingham New Street, where I had to run up and down the stairs to catch the connection, and the train was so packed I had to stand until Stafford, and then a pregnant woman got on just as I sat down and I had to pretend that I hadn't seen her, and when I forgot and caught her eye had to make out my leg was crippled.

It took me six hours to get there, despite, or probably because of, the £142 billion the government's spent on renewing the West Coast Line.

I was a bundle of nerves, I can't deny it. If only I could have spoken to Diane on the phone, just to break the ice. It had been 22 years since I'd seen her, for godsake.

Kurt had given me her address, somewhere in a place called Granton, which according to the map at the back of my Macmillan Encyclopaedia is miles from the centre of Edinburgh, and though he'd bought my train ticket, which was good of him, he hadn't lent me the fare for a taxi, and I spent a lot of the journey working out whether I should go by bus, which was slow and difficult and I'd probably have to change buses and I didn't know Edinburgh so I'd have to ask someone which bus to get and I find the Scottish accent can be quite impenetrable sometimes. Or get a taxi, which is expensive but easy.

I'd decided on a taxi, but then, such is the ever fertile mind of the creative writer, couldn't help but imagine my arrival at her house. Should I tell the taxi driver he ought to wait, or he could go? Well of course I should tell him to go, unhesitatingly, and then I imagined my knock on the door, and how would she look? Would she still be as gorgeous as she was, or would 22 years have given her a double chin, wrinkles, drooping cheeks? And how would I greet her? A smile and a little kiss, or a full hug, or would we on seeing each other know that this was what we were destined for, and fall into each other's arms and kiss passionately?

I had to get up and go to the buffet for a drink to calm my nerves, and forgot to limp, and the pregnant woman looked at me so furiously I had to pretend my leg was suddenly better and I was offering her my seat out of gallantry.

There were a few people in the buffet, Scots, and we had a few tins together, which was enjoyable, and stopped me thinking about Diane and running through different scenarios in my head, but they got out at Carstairs Junction to go to Glasgow, so I had a lonely last half-hour approaching Edinburgh, drinking on my own.

At Waverley Station I felt better. It was a sunny day, and I rather liked the city, lots of trees, open, pleasant architecture, and I thought, yes, if it comes to it, if it all works out between Diane and me, and from what Kurt said she was very keen, and

The beauty that is Edinburgh *

---

*   *Pleasant architecture, I said! All right, I did notice that one or two people had been drinking a little too much, but why dwell on the bad things? It's this cynicism that Connolly continually shows that I deplore. Where's the grace and the joy in his drawings that would be appropriate to my words? That's what I want to know.*

I couldn't really do much worse, then yes, I could live here.

I had a couple of pints of Tennents in a pub on Princes Street, just to get the feel of the place, and took the taxi out to Granton. Unfortunately, I got another attack of nerves, and asked him to drop me off just round the corner from her street, so I could walk the last few yards.

It was a fairly drab area, to be honest, a busy road with Victorian terraces opposite concrete shops and a boarded up warehouse. The road that Diane's house was on seemed quieter, and slightly more pleasant, with a few trees.

I saw a pub across the street, and thought I'd just settle myself down with a swift half before going to her house. It was fairly grotty outside, and inside wasn't much better, but there were a few men standing around with their pints of 80/-, which I thought I'd try, and they began chatting to me, asking where I was from, and what football team I supported, and I have to say they were very good fun, and their accents were not totally impenetrable, and I stayed there till three, when they left, and I found myself out on the street, trying to remember where I was and what I was doing there.

I sat on a little low wall outside the pub, and stared across to Diane's road, and I thought of her, and I realised, with that sudden knowledge that only seems to arrive after a little bit of alcohol has entered the bloodstream:

You can't turn the clock back.

She was then, and I was now, and she was over there, and I was over here.

And gorgeous or gone to seed, we weren't right for each other, and never would be, not now, though 22 years ago we might have been.

So I sighed for what was lost, and got on a bus which said City Centre, and went back to Waverley Station, and got the next train to Birmingham, only to find that Kurt had, rather foolishly, only bought me a single, despite my insisting I wanted a return, to keep my options open. It was okay, though, because the train was so full I went straight to the buffet, and when the ticket inspector came along managed to hide in the crowd, the inspector obviously not wanting to hang around in there too long.

From Birmingham there wasn't an inspector, though I had Kurt's name prepared if I was asked. I arrived home just before midnight, feeling a little sad that my life hadn't changed in the way I had expected, and I was to continue my solitary course, but invigorated by the day out.

Which I told Kurt, the next day, when I saw him in the Golden Lion. I think he must have been out looking for me, he was so keen to talk to me.

"How was it?" he said, with a little grin.

I thanked him, and told him that I thought Edinburgh was a pretty good place, with some pretty good people.

"With Diane!" he said, impatiently.

I explained that I had thought it over very carefully, and decided not to call on Diane.

His reaction was most peculiar. To call it ballistic would underestimate the power of the average rocket.

He started shouting.

"You didn't call on her? You stupid ******!" (I won't use his exact words, my publishers also publish scriptural treatises and wouldn't like it) "You absolute *******!"

Now I knew he'd spent £75 on a train ticket for me, for which I was very grateful, but it was only a loan, he knew that. Yes, he'd spent some time arranging for Diane and me to meet again. But this reaction was out of all proportion. I began to wonder, unless he just cared a lot about other people's happiness, if he was mentally ill.

Of course it would have made sense if he had been a writer, and was threequarters through his autobiography and needed a good ending, and wanted to find out how Diane and I would have got on.

I tried to calm him down by saying that I had very nearly reached the door of Diane's house, but had made a perfectly rational decision, weighed up with some care, that it would be better if I didn't knock on her door.

Then, he said:

"She's not there, you ******* ****!"

This made a little more sense, assuming he meant, "She's not all there", and that perhaps she'd had some kind of breakdown, and needed someone to care for her, and he and she had hoped I would be that person. But it only made me more glad that I hadn't knocked on her door. And he should have told me that before I travelled all that way. I mean, as it happened, I'd had a great day, thoroughly enjoyed myself and met a lot of interesting people. But he wasn't to know that.

Kurt stormed off, and I could see why he and Diane had got together in the first place. They were probably a couple of nutters. Although I only have his word that she's a nutter. Perhaps, to him, the sanest person is a nutter. Perhaps he thinks I'm a nutter!

I should be careful how I treat Kurt in the future.

But it was an example of a day well spent. In retrospect it would seem to have no purpose, in fact if Kurt had arranged to make me go to the furthest place possible on a wild goose chase, he couldn't have done better, on the surface.

But as it turned out I now think I may have enough material, having mastered the language, and if I can just finish *Trainspotting* (and I'd like to know if anyone's managed to finish *Trainspotting*) to write a **How To Write The Modern Drugtaking Scottish Novel**. Though the Edinburgh drugs of choice, in my experience, are a swally and a dram and a Regal Blue.

In conclusion, be Zen about your day. If that means studious sloth, writing a three word sentence that the next day you strike out as being too verbose, be content. Great Art cannot be forced like a cucumber.

Look, if you had a day when your book wrote itself, 5000 words of glorious prose, so good you could sleep for the first time in 25 years without hoping you'd die in your sleep to spare yourself the misery of a blank screen and its attendant feelings of worthlessness, then the next day — I guarantee — you would suffer for it.

"Why isn't it easy, like it was yesterday?" you'd say.

Because it was too easy, yesterday! You were too disciplined, and you can't hold your stomach flat forever, and when you let it out it'll plop over your belt even worse than before.

Relax. Go to the pub. Play *Civ IV*. Watch TV, especially if you're lucky enough to have Sky and can channel hop for six hours.

You've only got one life. Probably. Why worry about achieving anything?

That's what I realised, as I made my way back to Waverley Station, in Edinburgh's fair city:

You can only be unhappy if, for even one moment, you believe happiness is possible.

It's a great weight off my shoulders, to realise it isn't.

chapter thirteen

Writer's block

This is the picture non-writers have of Writer's Block: the author enters the room, sits at his or her desk, gets out a newly sharpened HB pencil and piece of paper, lifts the pencil to write, and finds he or she cannot physically make the pencil touch the paper. Or, these days, turns on the computer, opens Word, New document, blank screen, and the finger is poised but it just won't move down onto the keyboard.

People think it's like a disease, a paralysis of the hand. Everything else is fully functional but there's a kind of force field between finger and keys or between pen and page.

Amazing what the average punter thinks. Because that's exactly what writer's block is.

This is what happens to me: I get back from the pub and my brain is teeming with words. There are almost too many, there's a whole book in there. Except I can't start now, it's too late and I haven't the energy. But I'm still confident when I get up in the morning, or early afternoon. I know it's all there, the neurons are firing as they should.

I sit down. I'm ready, the book's already completed, it just needs the simple and almost automatic process of transferring from brain to page.

But it refuses to cross over. Even though the entire work is in my brain. Every word is there and ready.

Except one.

The first word.

Get that down, even if it's only "The" or "I" or "A", and the rest will follow. But though you're fairly sure it's "He", you're not absolutely certain. And unless you're absolutely certain you daren't start. Begin your greatest opus with the wrong word?

What a disaster! Everything else would come out in the wrong order then. Or, even worse, you'd have to cross it out, and just imagine when the manuscript is handed over to the professors of English at Oxford University, and they eagerly but carefully unpack the brown paper.

"At last, ladies and gentlemen, we have in our possession the first draft of what is undoubtedly the greatest How To Write Book that has ever been written."

They proudly look at the folder, then with padded tweezers gently open the first page. There's a horrified gasp as they see: "He" has been crossed out, and substituted with "They".

After the hubbub dies down the professor announces, "Perhaps we need to take a little time to reconsider this work in the pantheon."

Nods of agreement all round, as they quickly wrap up the manuscript again and hand it over to an assistant to put in the storage space up in the loft.

FACT BOX 31

You may think this problem doesn't happen now that no one uses a pen or pencil, but unfortunately the computer will store every deletion and amendment the writer makes in his Word document, and the academics of Oxbridge, disappointed authors themselves, will search through the code until they uncover your every secret.

I've tried many methods to break The Block, like doodling in the corner so the page isn't blank, or writing a selection of first words, one word to each page, so that I could later destroy the pages that I didn't use, but it doesn't help. There are too many alternatives, and seeing them spread out on your desk, or as ten different open documents on the laptop, makes it worse. The blankness of the page seems even larger and whiter and more of an accusation, like having ten children in order to only allow one to live.

The tricky first page *

The lucky painter, I always think, who can start with a splash of colour wherever he wants because it'll all get covered up in the end.

I don't know what the answer is. If I knew what the answer was I wouldn't tell you, I'd be in the Caribbean living off my millions-a-day royalties. Just keep staring at the screen till your eyes or mind go, whichever is first. That's another reason computer games are so useful, they break up that whiteness.

Of course I'm only talking about *First Page Writer's Block* here. If by some fluke you get over that you'll probably get

---

*   *This is what I mean about Connolly. How much is he getting paid? If he's getting money for each drawing and he claims for this I shall protest to the publishers in the strongest terms.*

struck down by *Mid-Work Writer's Block*. This occurs suddenly
and without warning. You've got past *First Page Writer's Block*,
you've finished the first chapter, you've finished the first 10
chapters, it's going well, the fingers are tapping, the words are
appearing on the screen, everything is great, and your mind
wanders, just a fraction. You think, "The publishers will love
this." Or: "This is just writing itself." Or: "This is so bloody
good I think I'll be up for an award."

And your fingers stop.

What was I writing? You look at the words you've just typed.
They don't make any sense.

"They don't make any sense," you've just typed. What the
hell was that about? No, it certainly doesn't make any sense.
You read back over the page, but it still doesn't make any sense.

All right, you need a rest. You have a coffee. You do The
Times crossword. You have a lie down. You go for a walk.

You come back. You look at the screen. You haven't a clue.

This version of *Mid-Work Writer's Block* I call *The
Complacency Syndrome*. You relaxed too soon. Relax when it's finished. Relax when it's all sent off and you're about to start your
next book and have to prepare yourself to face *First Page Writer's
Block* again.

Nothing writes itself, you pillock. If it wrote itself you'd be
nothing better than a robot or a computer program. It's only
because this work has been squeezed through the torture of
having every word searched out that it is as wonderful as it is.

External Factor Writer's Block: that's another one. That has a
whole list of subdivisions, the most common of which is *Mobile
Phone External Factor Writer's Block*.

It goes like this: somehow you've got past *First Word Writer's
Block*. Somehow you've avoided, so far, *Mid-Work (Complacency
Syndrome) Writer's Block*. It's Monday morning, always a difficult
time, because your head hasn't quite returned to normal, or it
has returned to normal and you'd preferred it hadn't. You've
delayed turning on the laptop for as long as possible by having
six coffees (until you ran out of milk), went for a walk (to get
some more milk), did The Times crossword (well not all of it,

about six clues, but you don't believe anyone in the world ever finishes it, since those six clues took three hours), but finally you think you're ready to continue chapter 13, Writer's Block.

The laptop is on, and you remind yourself where you were, "Ah yes, just writing about *Mobile Phone External Factor Writer's Block*." You were just about to explain what happens on a Monday, after you've spent most of the day readying yourself like an athlete for an Olympic final, and you're ready, you've warmed up, you're under starter's orders, the words are about to flow, when

That was Laura's solicitor. Why Laura feels she can't talk to me in person I don't know.

What was I saying?

I can't remember.

It's put me right off, that has. I don't know why I keep my mobile switched on. I ought to just turn it on when I want to call someone. Except I live in hope that some friend might feel I'm worth sparing a couple of minutes in the day just to inquire how I am, or a publisher might ring to offer me a wonderful new book deal.

But no.

It's a bloody solicitor.

I hate solicitors.

Them, and estate agents, and doctors, and teachers, and tax inspectors, and traffic wardens, and the police.

We were married for eight years, for goodness sake, Laura and me. Doesn't that mean anything? That works out at about 3000 times we lay together in the same bed. Surely that should mean something.

Think of all those intimate moments we shared. The mutual confessions. Those times I'll never forget, like the birth of our boys. Well, the birth of Jordan, I missed Adam, but that wasn't my fault, it was a Saturday night, and I certainly wouldn't have been in the pub if I'd realised he was going to arrive a day early.

And after all that she uses a solicitor to threaten me. It's ruined the whole day for me. I can't write any more. I can't even remember what I was saying.

He wouldn't even let me put my side of the case. He wasn't interested. Snooty bastard. The thing is, I know this man. I played badminton against him once. It was a doubles match, and there was a crucial point, at 13 all, and he hit the shuttlecock, and I left it, and called it out.

It was my call. That's understood, in badminton. If it's on your side it's your call. And maybe it just sneaked onto the line. Maybe. Just. I thought he couldn't see, because I'd put myself between him and where it landed, but when I looked round he was further across than I thought and actually had a very good view.

Barry Mickelson, he's called, and I don't believe he ever forgave me for that. I never forgave him for never forgiving me, anyway, because what a petty thing not to forgive someone for, a genuine mistake like that.

FACT BOX 32

Scientists now think that they've discovered the cause of Writer's Block:

It's a virus, similar to the one that affects golfers with the yips, twitches, and jerks, where they can't swing the putter evenly, and darts players with the stutters, staggers, and jitters, where the hand is unable to release the dart.

If it is a virus it would explain why this occurs to me even on days when I'm taking antibiotics for some unrelated illness, an ear infection, say, because antibiotics don't kill viruses, only bacteria.

Of course, this explanation only relates to First Page Writer's Block and Mid-Work (Complacency Syndrome) Writer's Block, and not Mobile Phone External Factors Writer's Block.

Reference: Nature, July 2002 (or so bozzo35 from the newsgroup alt.conspiracy.theories said)

The way he talked to me, just now, on the phone was like we'd never met. All cold and legal.

And yes, as it happens, Mr Snooty Solicitor Barry Mickelson, I do consider *Grand Theft Auto Vice City* a suitable computer game for a eight-year-old.

I played on it first, and thoroughly enjoyed it. All this hysteria whipped up about computer games. They used to say it about TV when I was young, and the cinema when my parents were young, and probably Jacobean theatre when Barry Mickelson was young, if he ever was.

At first I thought it was about the fact that the copy of *Grand Theft Auto* was pirated, and that could have landed me in trouble, and I did feel bad about that, because I'm very hot on plagiarism. Though the makers of *Grand Theft Auto* probably paid their writers off with a lump sum, and the writers are the ones I'm thinking of.

But how are our children going to learn about life if they're always shielded from its nasty side? And actually, gunning down a rival gangster as he lies pleading for his life is most satisfying. As is driving a truck into a bus queue. It helps get rid of aggression.

I shouldn't have had to defend myself. Not to that creep, anyway. They're my sons, I can bring them up how I want. And if I can't, I ought to be able to. I'm going to have to join that Fathers For Justice group, and abseil down Canary Wharf dressed as Spiderman. If I had a head for heights.

Laura and I used to get on so well, too. I remember one day, before we were married, of course, and we both took a day off work. You know, she rang my school and I rang her office and we both said the other was ill, and we just spent the whole day in the park walking by the river and chatting and feeding the birds, it was a freezing day, and then we went to the pub.

What a great day that was. We didn't argue. We didn't criticise. We enjoyed each other's company, and that's how it should always have been. Except that when I suggested we do it the next day she refused, because she said she hadn't liked the feeling that someone from work might have seen her. So she even managed to spoil that lovely day we had together, and it was downhill from then on.

I can't remember the number of times I'd be lying next to her, and I'd think, of all the girls in the world, why did I marry her?

I believe that's a bad sign, in a marriage.

chapter fourteen

Your audience

There's one method I know for a How to Write writer to ensure the effects of Writer's Block are alleviated as much as possible, and that's to ask yourself, and answer, the question: "Who is your audience?"

Well. Go on. Ask yourself.

Who's your audience?

I'll tell you.

It's yourself, 10 or 20 or 30 years ago. It's you as an adolescent, beginning to realise that now's the time to put away your much loved and read copy of *The Wind in the Willows*, and enter a new world of literature.

So you read James Patterson and Nick Hornby and Ian Rankin, but decide, after a while, that those gaudy covers don't look good on the bus or train or in the canteen, and certainly aren't impressing anyone. So you decide it's about time you were taken a little more seriously, by your friends and family. It's time you became: *an intellectual*.

You buy books by Kafka, and Gabriel Garcia Marquez, and Carlos Fuentes, and anyone else with a foreign sounding name who sounds like they've won the Nobel prize, and you begin to dream of being the British Murakami or Saramagao, and how even your sisters, who treat you like a little squirt, would be impressed by that.

You hold your head up a little higher, listen to Beethoven's string quartets, and start to write your acceptance speech.

There's only one snag. What are you going to write, and how are you going to write it?

That's the person you're writing for, the young you, full of dreams about how easy it's going to be, how every short story will be pored over by literary reviewers and academics, every novel published to applause and profiles in the broadsheet newspapers, every screenplay filmed by Ken Loach, every play performed simultaneously in every capital city of the world.

What does that young idealistic person need? He needs a book to tell him he's full of bullshit. He needs to be told: "It isn't like that, mate. It's bloody hard. You're going to be rejected so many times you'll feel the whole world is spitting on you. You'll be lucky to get a joke printed in Reader's Digest."

They'll thank you for it in the end.

My nephew Jason came and saw me a few years ago. He's my eldest sister's boy. A nice lad, good-looking, confident, well spoken. He made a special visit, when I was still at home, because he wanted to be a writer, and needed an agent.

That's what he said.

I told him: "You can't get an agent until you've had something published, and you can't get anything published unless you've got an agent. It's a fact of life. Just forget about writing," I said, "and concentrate on the computer programming."

That's what he did, then, computer programming, and he was very good at it, and seemed to earn a decent amount. He had a very pretty girlfriend, he brought her along that day, dark hair, lovely eyes, 21 and gorgeous. Holly, her name was. It wasn't the fact that she was there I was telling him this. I wasn't trying to put him down and impress her with my worldly knowledge. I was just telling him the truth.

He nodded, and seemed to take on board what I was saying.

He split up from that girl not long after, I heard. I wished I'd got her phone number, because by the way she was looking at me I'm sure she was impressed by my worldly knowledge.

Anyway, I heard from my sister that Jason had given up trying to publish his 'novel', which I was pleased about, for his sake.

Then a year later she told me he had adapted it as a screenplay and it was going to be made by Channel 4! Not a word of thanks to me. I saw it, when they finally showed it.

Sadly, I wasn't very impressed, even if the critics did seem to rave about it. But they're all the same age, aren't they? 25 and know nothing about life. It's this youth culture we have. If you're over 30 you might as well be dead.

Piddock's nephew, Jason *

They have competitions, for young writers. If you're younger than 21, send in your play/story/poem. We'd love to hear from you. Illiteracy no bar.

If it was up to me, and I had a spare £5,000, I'd have a competition to stop young people sending in their plays and

---

* All right, Jason is a very equable young man, and he is doing quite well in television (the medium I and most other proper writers have always rather despised). But we don't want to see a drawing of him in this book. I'd rather have that blank picture from the previous chapter, frankly. Not that I begrudge Jason's slight success. Not at all.

stories and poems. Young people are not interesting. They haven't done anything. Well, nothing that I didn't do when I was their age, anyway.

If it were possible, I'd ban young people writing words out of school or college. Let them send text messages. That should be the limit of their verbal dexterity.

With most of them it is. They can hardly talk, but they want to write a novel. Wait till you've got some experience!

FACT BOX 33

If you are around the age of 20, then stop reading this book right now. Leave a marker at this page, put the book on your bookshelf, in a fairly prominent position, and in 15 years' time pick it up again and carry on reading from here, because by then it will be relevant to you.

I always enjoy seeing Jason's name mentioned. He gets quite a lot of stuff put on TV these days, although I'm afraid a lot of it is the Casualty/EastEnders type of 'drama', which doesn't interest me. I like Coronation Street, of course, but that's got some humour in it, and real people.

But, and I'm sure he won't mind me saying this, I do wonder what Jason could have become, if he hadn't gone down that path. If he'd waited. The work he might have produced.

Of course, he makes a lot of money, and I wouldn't mind a hundredth of his yearly income. They just throw it out, on TV. Write a two-minute sketch on TV and you can pay off your mortgage.

I haven't seen Jason since Laura and I split up. Most of my family took her side, which was rather unfair. I did send him a birthday card last year, jocularly asking him for the name of his agent. I thought that would amuse him. And I thought he might tell me. I could do with an agent. They are useful, and I am a published author.

I didn't hear from him.

But that's the kind of person who you should be thinking of as you write your How To Write Book, someone fairly young, doesn't have much natural talent, is rather derivative and unimaginative, but is good-looking, which works well on the back of a dust jacket.

It's you, around the age of 20.

Now picture yourself at that age, still slightly spotty, but able for some weird biological reason to get the girls of your age to be your girlfriend, when if they had any sense they'd be looking for someone a lot older. Done that? Pictured yourself? Not pleasant, is it? Never mind. What I want you to do is talk to yourself.

I don't mean talk to yourself as in witter away like a loony. I mean address that person that you once were. Have a conversation with him.

I find it works a treat. You can get that superior edge in your voice, which is very important in a How To Write Book. You can be gently deprecating about their hopes and dreams, knowing as you do what a balls-up they're going to make of their life.

Now you should see how useful such advice is. I can't see that a Time Machine will ever be invented, because we'd have noticed if there were people from the future walking around like Star Trek extras, unless they thought the 2000s weren't worth visiting, but I can well see the time when information could be transmitted to the past. Much simpler, I'm sure, than trying to transport a body. You've just got to send a radio signal, via some black hole or other (I leave the technical details to the scientists, though hope they acknowledge it as my idea).

Imagine the benefits to humanity. You could bet on a particular horse winning a particular race. You could watch a TV programme before it had been broadcast. You could even send back the instructions for building a time information device, so it could be built right now! Which means you wouldn't need to wait for one to be built.

Wait a minute. This is why I didn't become a scientist. These kind of discussions give me a headache.

But just imagine the greatest use of an information-send-ing-back-in-time device: *Telling yourself who to marry.* Or better, who not to marry. "It didn't work out," you say to your earlier self. "She's going to turn out to be a shrew who leaves you for a friend," you could say. For example. And your younger self would thank you, and when he saw that girl he'd think, "How could I have ever married you? Well thank God I'm not going to," and he'd never talk to her again, despite her begging him to tell her, "What have I done, what have I done?"

Except, of course, young people being how they are, stub-born and arrogant, he'd ignore the advice, and say, "She won't turn into a shrew. She won't leave me for a friend. I'm differ-ent. I'm in love!"

I can see it in my two boys, and they're only five and eight. They're already past that time when I could set them on my knee and tell them about the Tooth Fairy or Santa Claus. Now, they know best, and don't believe a word I say.

FACT BOX 34

Mind you, Adam, he's the eight-year-old, he's got a great right foot. I think he could become a professional foot-baller. I always wanted to be a professional footballer, when I was his age. We have some great games of football together, the three of us. Well, until they do something silly, like kick the ball away just as you're running up to take a penalty. That sort of behaviour really annoys me, especially when I could have got hurt, and I feel I have no choice but to send them inside. Which is a shame, because I was enjoying it. But you mustn't change your mind, as a parent, or they won't respect you.

It doesn't last long, the trust that children give their par-ents. They grow up in their own way, and it is important to see them as independent beings, and not people that can fulfil your lost dreams for you.

I realise this chapter has been slanted towards males, for which I apologise, but my advice still holds if you're female: just imagine that your younger self is the reader. The difference is that I don't find girls around the age of 20 to be at all stubborn or arrogant, so I think you can give good advice, and they'll take it.

Just tell them not to bother with those callow youths they hang around with, but to seek out the man with a little more experience and knowledge of the world. Apparently, I read somewhere, it's an evolutionary device, younger women liking slightly older men, because the women are looking for men who have proved that their genes are worth having. So it's not something unnatural or unhealthy, it's actually very desirable for both parties.

Like the barmaid down the Golden Lion, Drusilla. I talk to her a lot, and she's very sweet, about 19, quite intelligent, and you might think that someone like her, pretty and young, and someone like me, 45 or so (though I've been taken for 39), would not be a good match. On the contrary. Our children would be good-looking, and have the benefit of my teachings. She would look up to me and do what I suggested, while not expecting me to go dancing with her at a club until three o'clock in the morning.

It would be perfect.

But not a bit of it. I'm talking to her quite meaningfully, about, say, my financial difficulties, or the problems I have with Laura and the children, and some youth walks into the pub, with greasy dreadlocks and a stud in his nose and patches of down on his cheeks, and she's all over him, lending him money, letting him have a drink without paying, arranging to meet him afterwards, and telling me, when he's gone, how gorgeous he is.

"I don't think so," I tell her. "You're gorgeous. *He's* a disgusting lout."

She doesn't even hear me. She doesn't react, anyway. Actually, I probably haven't spoken the words, just thought them loudly.

Now I don't believe there's a sexist bone in my body, but I do believe that all young men are stupid and think they're wonderful, and all young women think they're stupid and are wonderful.

It's true. Women are just a lot nicer than men (obviously one has to exclude the women one has ever been married to, obviously).

And because of this, I have to say that my advice to you about advising your younger self not to write is a thousand times more pertinent for women than men.

I'm sorry, but it's a fact: the only reason that you, as a 20-year-old woman, will ever get a book published is because the publishers can put your beautiful full face — or even more beautiful full body in revealing black dress — photo filling the entire back of the dust jacket. That's not me being sexist, that's the publishing industry. No one wants to read what a girl's written. I don't, anyway. Why does she think anyone else does? It can't be because she's arrogant, because she's not.

It's because some dirty old man of an agent has told her that she's a great writer, just so he can get her into bed, and now he's had to pay for the book to appear in print so he doesn't seem to be a brazen bastard.

There's no other reason. Not that I can think of.

I hope this chapter has made planning and starting your How To Write Book a little easier. You may be tempted, if you met your younger self, to give him or her a good belt round the head. But be patient. There, but for the grace of God, went you.

When I was about 17 I saw the careers master at school. He was also my maths teacher. He was quite a good teacher, if impatient and lacking a sense of humour.

He asked me what I wanted to be, and I proudly said (because it's something I've always been proud of, and rightly): "I'm going to be a writer."

He suggested I get a job with a local newspaper, as a start. "No," I said. "A writer. Not a journalist." My parents had always read the *Daily Mail*, so I knew the difference, even then.

He still thought it was a good idea. "You'll meet people, find out how they live, get lots of good stories." But, when he saw I had no intention of taking his advice, he said, "Well, whatever you do, don't become a maths teacher, because you'll regret every moment."

And those words of his — and how true they were — stuck with me, throughout the 12 years I spent teaching maths.

chapter fifteen

Presentation

B y now, if you've been paying attention and have followed the guidance I've given you in this book, you should have almost finished your very own How To Write Book.

You've got the title, and the chapters, and the words in the chapters, but what you're not sure of is how to present your work to a publisher or agent. That's what this chapter is all about, and if you stick to my suggestions the finishing touches will make that difference between the publisher's reader chucking the manuscript straight into the skip, or sitting up, waving your book, and shouting round the office, "We've got our next big hit right here!"

Firstly, break it up. No one, not even a professional editor and a publishing company, can read page after page of words. Just think how difficult reading is, anyway. The speed with which you have to interpret each tiny squiggle, put the squiggle together to make words, put the words together to make sentences, put the sentences together to realise what the hell the author means.

You know, now I think about it, it makes me dizzy. It's almost supernatural. It seems, on the face of it, impossible. How does it work? Maybe there's some device they haven't found yet, between the eye and brain, a little optical character recognition device, that interprets what you're reading, so really all you're doing is scanning.

That would make more sense than any traditional idea of reading, which is, when you consider it objectively, completely unfeasible.

But, however it works, do help the reader.

Short paragraphs are useful. They allow you to state things

clearly.

But beware:

Don't have too many.

Or it'll begin to look like a poem.

And everyone glazes over

With poetry.

Fact Boxes are wonderful. I love Fact Boxes. Turn a page and see a Fact Box and you feel good about the page. You think, shall I finish this paragraph, or go straight to the Fact Box? I'll go straight to the Fact Box, because it's bound to have something interesting in it. Well, more interesting than this paragraph, anyway.

And it always does.

FACT BOX 35

There are two alternative theories as to the birth of Fact Boxes. English historians say that when the King James Bible was first printed the King felt that the Ten Commandments were not prominent enough, as bullet points and bold type hadn't been invented. So, to make them clearer for the second edition, the printer surrounded them with lines of type, and now no one could miss them. Though, let's face it, the Ten Commandments are hardly facts, and that is important, obviously, in a Fact Box.

I enthused, once, about Fact Boxes to Ryan Jinks. He thought they could be overdone. Obviously, I said, they can be overdone. Anything can be overdone. But they are useful. Very useful. Even vital.

Look at Ryan's *Writing a Big Science-Fiction Novel*, and you'll see plenty of Fact Boxes. Just another unacknowledged help he's taken from me. Apart from the whole idea of the book. It's certainly not his best, though, and that's not saying much.

I once happened to be in his house, it was during a barbecue he had, everyone was outside in the garden and I came in to go to the loo, and I noticed his study door was open, and I thought I'd check his manuscript of *Writing a Big Science-Fiction Novel* for him, as it was almost finished.

When I brought it up on his computer, I was stunned. He didn't have a single Fact Box.

He adds them in later!

This, to me, is criminal. It's as if in *War and Peace* Tolstoy had added in the Napoleonic wars later, or Shakespeare wrote *Hamlet* and then thought, "Oh, I could have a Prince of Denmark in this play."

Don't skimp on the Fact Boxes, and don't add them in later. Every couple of pages, write a Fact Box. You'll enjoy writing them as much as your reader will enjoy reading them. It gives everyone a break.

Incidentally, there was an amusing sequel to my visit to Ryan's study that time. The next day, when I saw Ryan in the Bell, he was frothing at the mouth because somehow the file containing his final draft of *Writing a Big Science-Fiction Novel*, and all his previous drafts, and the backups he kept on a different hard drive, had been deleted, and, foolishly, he hadn't printed out a copy, or made a back-up on a separate disk.

It was very unlucky for him, although he learnt a good lesson that day. Always back up your work! He had to rewrite the whole thing from scratch, which is not an easy thing to do, as it takes twice as much energy as the initial writing (so I hear — I've never had to do it).

I didn't take advantage of his misfortune, and hurry on with my own **How To Write a High Concept Science-Fiction Novel**, as I was having a lot of problems with a certain telecom company at the time, problems which I later used to good effect as the basis for my ***How To Write a Stinking Letter of Complaint***, the work of mine which probably gave me most pleasure to write, even if I was advised by a lawyer acquaintance that I should remove all the references to that certain telecom company based in this country and which used to have a monopoly on our telephones until it was privatised and which still rings me up asking if I'd like to revise my Friends and

Family list even though I only have a mobile phone.

I still wish I could have kept those references in. I felt it was vital to the work. I just wanted to sting them, with all their billions of pounds profit a year and they threaten me just for owing them a couple of hundred pounds.

FACT BOX 36

O n the other hand, Italian historians claim that Fact Boxes were invented about half a century previously, in Milan, when a local printer found he had a pile of capital I's left over after printing Dante's Divine Comedy, and his son made a square with them at the bottom of a page. In that case, the box was purely decorative and left empty, but soon other printers had the idea that they could fill the box with an interesting fact. So, the Fact Box was born.

I'm still convinced, too, that that bill was the product of one of those premium dialling services infiltrating the computer I had. It was certainly nothing to do with me accessing any dubious sites on the internet. As I used to tell Laura, when she asked me why I was downstairs until 2.30 in the morning, it was research.

And, no, I didn't know where those credit card payments came from, but it must have been some kind of mistake, although a mistake that wasn't worth following up because those sort of sites are all obviously illegal and untraceable.

Laura was never very good with computers. I had to explain every little technical thing to her, and she still didn't understand them. Not that that stopped her accusations. Perhaps I was rather short tempered with her about it, but it was a difficult time for me, with the person I thought was a friend stealing my ideas and livelihood.

I don't think she appreciated the stress that a writer feels. She'd go on about her boss asking her to work overtime, and the dangers of the unprotected machinery in the factory, while

I had the far greater worry of where my next How To Write Book was coming from, since I'd given up teaching.

She certainly expressed no understanding in my battle for justice against Ryan Jinks. I told her, the man was threatening my very existence. She couldn't see it like that. She always took his side. Of course, only now do I see why she always took his side, but then I was a loving and trusting husband, even if I was being driven by her out to the pub, night after night, to try and seek some sympathy with my companions there.

I mean driven out in the sense of pushed out of the house. She didn't actually drive me in the car. Though that would have been nice, as it was almost half a mile to the pub.

Actually, it was there, in the pub, one night, that I discovered the truth about Laura, though, of course, I would never put that in a book such as this one.

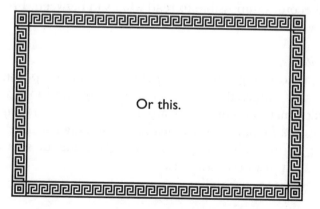

Have bold little statements.
That's another very useful way of breaking up a page, and giving the reader's eyes, or optical character recognition faculties,
a rest.

But again, not too many.
Or it becomes impossible to read what's in between. I find that
anyway.

I hate italics.
I can't read them. Whenever there's an italicised passage in a
book, my internal optical character recognition scanner
doesn't function. The italics are saying, *This is very important,
you must read this, even if you don't read anything else.* And I can't
read it, because it's so important. It's like someone shouting in
your ear. It just becomes noise.

Never, *ever*, use italics.

BLOCK CAPITALS ARE EVEN WORSE. THEY ARE IMPOSSIBLE TO READ. THEY'RE NOT SHOUTING, THEY'RE *SHRIEKING*.

Subheadings

I'm not convinced about subheadings.

Or sub-sub headings

I mean, you can take it too far.

Or even sub sub sub headings

And they take too much thought, frankly, even if they do stretch out a page quite nicely.

Brackets

You should only use brackets when what you want to say is too short to put in a Fact Box. Otherwise you're depriving everyone.

Square Brackets

These are different to rounded brackets! Beware Square Brackets. They are only *ever* used when you are making a note for your editor or printer, and they will not appear in the final work. For example, if I wrote:

[*The spelling of this must be checked*]

— that would not be printed. Obviously, it's vital the writer and printer know this, and doesn't use square brackets in the wrong place.

[*Note to the printer: those last square brackets should appear, as they are an example*]

[*but not the ones after*]

[*or these, or any further ones, unless I specifically say otherwise*]

Empty space
Leave some blank space when you need to fill a chapter and can't think of anything more to write, and say it's useful blank space for the reader to make notes.

Like here!

(only do this if you're really desperate)

Well, what happened in the pub that night, I made some mention of Ryan Jinks, and everyone laughed. I asked them why they'd laughed, and they just laughed again. Well, naturally, I got suspicious about this, that they knew something that I didn't. There was no reason for them to laugh, not that I knew of. And I realised. There was something going on, between Laura and Ryan. That was the only possible reason.

I told Mad Mac, a couple of days later, after I got over the initial shock. I told him I knew why they'd all laughed, when I mention Ryan.

He blustered, and tried to say it was because I was always going on about Ryan, but I knew that was a blatantly absurd cover up. I hardly ever mentioned Ryan. I had no reason to mention him. In fact, if I never mentioned him again it'd be too soon.

It was, as you can imagine, a terrible knowledge to have: that my wife and a fellow author — a, one might say, colleague

— were having an affair. It was a knowledge I almost wished I didn't have. But of course I realised how blind I'd been, as the signs were all there. The way she would always defend him, when any rational and unbiased person would have seen his actions as indefensible, and the rather formal way she would greet him, as if pretending that there was nothing between them.

However, I decided not to act straightaway, but to wait until I had more proof.

Other ways of presenting your work
- Use bullet points.
- There are a great variety of bullet points.
1. They can be numbered.
- Or have fancy little symbols.
- They also stretch the words.
- And no one could possibly think it's a poem.

Columns
Columns I have no time for. They look wrong. They're difficult to manage. And besides, I've never found out how to do them in Word.

Don't use columns.

Tables
Tables are easier. I do like to have tables mixed with boxes, with ticks all over the place.

	Look good	Easy to do
Tables	✓✓	✓
Columns	✗	✗✗✗✗
Fact Boxes	✓✓✓✓	✓✓✓✓

There are a lot of other ways of making your manuscript look good. Get a book on Word, or borrow one from the library. If you've got the time to read it. There are thousands of little tricks and formatting devices, but frankly, life's too short.

As an addendum to this chapter on **Presentation**, I have just found out something quite extraordinary.

I received an e-mail from my old University, with a newsletter containing information about people in my year.

It mentioned Diane.

And she lives in Melbourne, Australia, not Edinburgh, Scotland!

I suspect Kurt may be on drugs. Or certifiably mad. I don't know whether to search him out and confront him, or avoid him.

I wasn't mentioned in the newsletter, by the way. Although perhaps you have to submit the information yourself.

Diane is a dental assistant in Melbourne. Married, with four children. And if any of the old gang happen to find themselves out there, they're welcome to drop in. To Nunawading, Melbourne, Victoria, Australia.

Drop in!

Sometimes, I think the whole world has gone mad.

FACT BOX 37

And here's another thing to show everyone's mad:
I have just discovered that the Fact Boxes the 'designer' of this book has made aren't really boxes! They're just two lines. Two lines do not make a box! This is the trouble with designers. They have no idea. It's called minimalism, I believe. Well I call it laziness! First Connolly and his 'drawings', now this. I mean if I ask for a box, I want a box. Not two lines.

Honestly.

Spoilt my day, that has, finding that out.

That and about Diane.

Melbourne!

---

chapter sixteen

Submitting your idea

If you've followed the few simple rules I've laid out, you'll have a well bound and neatly printed manuscript on your desk, with an attractive cover and an alluring title and lots of Fact Boxes, and you're probably feeling rather pleased with yourself.

Well don't!

You think you've done the hard work? You think your troubles are over?

They've only just started. The hard work's only just begun. The pain and torment of creating your masterpiece is like a pinprick compared to being dismembered on the rack of trying to get it published.

What should you do?

You could shove it in an envelope, with a covering letter and return postage, and begin to send it to every publisher in the UK.

You could, but if you've got that much money to waste why not give it to a charity, Oxfam, say, or the Red Cross, or Action Aid? Or I can be contacted through my publishers, address at the front of this book. Send me your surplus pounds. I wouldn't mind some extra cash.

Believe me, no publisher will read a complete manuscript these days. They'll look at the title, the chapter list, the first page, and send it back. But because it's a complete manuscript, and the north wall of the reader's office is being supported by piles of manuscripts, they'll take a very long time doing it.

In fact, after they've kept your manuscript 10 years, they'll almost certainly bin it and keep the stamps, although by then inflation will mean they won't be worth enough for a second-class letter.

Don't send the complete manuscript. Just let them see the title, the list of chapters, and the first page. And — if you really want to get it published — say your name is Wayne Rooney.

If they don't fall for that, they'll then send it back, but a bit faster than if you'd sent them the complete manuscript.

FACT BOX 38

Elias Greensmith is in the Guinness Book of World Records as the author who had the longest time for a manuscript to be considered. He sent his wilderness thriller, Wolves of the Frozen North, to Chicago publishers Renwick & Lovering in 1953. They went bankrupt in 1966, and their offices were taken over by a law firm. The law firm moved out in 1972, and the offices were subsequently used by an estate agents, an insurance firm, a double glazing call centre, local Progressive Party headquarters, and the upstairs of a Chinese restaurant.

All the time Greensmith's manuscript lay, unlooked at, in the corner of a room. Finally, in 1996, the offices were rented by a publishing firm, publishers Provost & Son. In 2001, a full 38 years after Smith had submitted his work, they discovered Wolves of the Frozen North, read it, and — this is the amazing part — found that it was an unpublishable pile of garbage.

Look, let's face it, and I'm going to be entirely honest with you here, no matter how good your How To Write a Book is — brilliant title, well written, packed with good advice — no reputable publisher is going to bother with it. It's hard to accept, but it's true. You should have looked at this chapter before you started the book. I should have put this at the front, or on the cover, except then you wouldn't have bought the book. There is no way, these days, you're going to break into the coterie of published authors.

I couldn't get anywhere with *How To Write a Stinking Letter of Complaint*, and I'm an experienced and established and well reviewed How To Write writer with two How To Write Books already published! And not one of the bastards would even consider the book.

I did it all the right way. Sent a perfect letter describing how this book would finally put them, Mr or Mrs Publisher, on the world publishing map. They would be the envy of every other publisher. This was their dream manuscript. Put everything down, clear the presses, and get this one out into the bookshops before Christmas, because they were going to be very rich indeed. And yes, I would accept a five figure advance, as a down payment (you have to show confidence in your work, you see).

But one after the other the letter came back, the same letter I'd sent, usually with a scribbled, "Not for me, thanks," or, "No!!!!!!!!!!!!!!!!!!!", or even — as if there was no one in the office — nothing at all.

One letter had obviously been passed round the company, the number of rather unpleasant comments in different hands that had been put on it. For that one I took example 56 of my own book, "When obscene abuse is all you have left," and gave them a good blast up the backside. I ignored the legal letters that followed. Luckily I followed my own advice, and used a Post Office Box Number.

It was a great book, *How To Write a Stinking Letter of Complaint*, the one I think I enjoyed writing the most. It was so useful, that was what was particularly galling. It would have sold by the bucketload.

Eventually, after months of disappointment and rejections by about 30 obviously congenitally stupid publishers, I did something which I would not necessarily recommend. I decided to let someone I know look at it, so I could receive some kind of objective outsider's view.

Now I don't recommend this course of action for a number of reasons, including:

1.   I know a huge amount about How To Write Books.
2.   Everyone else knows squat about How To Write Books.

But sometimes there's no one else except friends you can turn to.

Of course, I couldn't let Laura look at it (this was before we separated). After all, there's a rule here:

RULE 7
Never let your spouse look at your work.

Why? Because there's too much jealousy there. They want you to succeed, to a certain extent — the extent, I suppose, of making a lot of money so they can go shopping in Laura Ashleys and Marks & Spencer. But they don't want you to have critical success. Going to ceremonies and meeting Kevin Spacey would be very nice, of course, but the shift in power in the relationship would be utterly unbearable to a spouse.

That is my experience, anyway.

So if she found the work to be brilliant, she wouldn't be able to bring herself to say so. And if she didn't like it, it'd be impossible to keep the gloat out of her voice. More likely, she'd relate it to our lives, and complain that some of the phrases I'd included were taken from arguments we had had, and she didn't think I should put our lives into print. Phrases like "boneheaded subhuman birdbrain", or "lardheaded numbskull". Even though they're some of the more affectionate, really.

No, spouses are not the people to share your work with. They may claim they've always admired your creative ability and the fact that it sets you apart from the rest of humanity, but actually that's the very thing they resent, deeply. They thrive on your failure. The further down you go, the more they rise.

So I couldn't show Laura my manuscript.

Who else, then? Not Ryan, not unless I wanted him to write a *The Craft of Writing a Big Complaining Letter*. Mum and Dad? But their reaction would be the mirror of the spouse problem

— instead of being overcritical, they'd be too nice, because parents are easily impressed.

It had to be someone from down the pub. Who was it to be? Rowdy Pete? Mad Mac? Dan the Van? Frank the Ape? Or Sam Sum?

Rowdy Pete is one of the quietest people I know (in case you're not clear, his nickname is ironic, you see), and very straight and very direct, but frankly not well educated. Sam Sum (who was my fellow maths teacher when I worked on the whiteboard face) is one of those outdoor types, very fit, very hearty, makes you sick, and has probably never read a word since he was at primary school. Jack the Hack is a journalist, so is similarly ignorant about the use of the English language. As is Dan the Van, the builder. Frank the Ape's the joker, always a witty quip on his lips. And Mad Mac is a cynical old buffer who argues with anyone and on principle will always tell them they're wrong.

Frankly I couldn't trust any of them, but I finally decided to honour Jack with the task, if such an enjoyable activity can be called a task.

I caught him in the pub on his own, one day, and bought him a drink. He feigned extreme surprise — he's got a good sense of humour — and asked what I was after. I can take a joke, so I explained that I'd like him to have a look at my latest opus. He seemed flattered that I'd chosen him, and said he would very much like to look at it.

I dropped it off at his house, and in the pub the next Saturday asked him what he thought. He said he hadn't had a chance to look at it but he would.

He repeated this the next four Saturdays, until, I suppose, he detected my increasing impatience.

"Well, to be honest," he said. "I have read it."

"Yes?" I said.

"And it's very well written. And looks very good. And reads well."

"That's what I thought," I said. "Well, it's what I knew, actually. Anything else?" I said, looking out for a Well done, or

You must be pleased (*see Fact Box 29*).

"Well," he said. " I just thought that in one or two places it was a bit over the top."

Over the top.

That's what he said.

Over the top.

Jack the Hack *

Well of course it was my fault for letting an amateur soil my manuscript, though I hadn't quite perceived the depths of his ignorance.

He said he'd got some other comments, but I refused to listen to him. I realised how deluded I was to think I'd get any

* *Another picture of someone completely peripheral to this book, even if it does show the state of his messy mind. But Jack's a journalist, for heaven's sake, and this is a book about writing. Get him out of here!*

useful advice from anyone. There's only one person whose advice I'd trust:

Me.

I wrote it. I know it's good, and useful, and if it ever appeared on the shelves in Smith's there'd be a queue of people punching each other on the nose to buy it. But that's what we How To Write writers are up against. Ignorance, and stupidity.

Well, you could be lucky. You might get it accepted. This book's in print, although if it hadn't been I would've blown up every publisher in central London [*that last phrase to be removed from the final proof*]. Ryan Jinks has had a couple of books published, although he probably had to sleep with all of the directors of his publishers' firm to do it. Even if they were male.

Especially if they were male!

So it is possible. Just very very unlikely. If you want to make some money, buy a lottery ticket. With the lottery, there's only a 14 million-to-one chance against.

Useful blank space at the end of the chapter
for you to make notes

(I'm not really desperate to find something to write, obviously. I'm only doing this to show you how annoying it is. And obvious. If a chapter is really short, it's just embarrassing to put something as feeble as this. Don't do it. Do anything, find some awful so-called artist to doodle in your book.)

(No, on second thoughts blank space is better than that.)

chapter seventeen

Publishers and agents

Some writers I know say that all publishers and agents are bloodsucking scum of the earth who live off the fruits of others, yet despise and drain the life force from the literary geniuses who do all the work.

I wouldn't make such a sweeping statement.

I once met someone in a publisher's office who was a decent person. She was only making the tea, but it did show me that there is some vestige of humanity in that rapacious and parasitical world.

I don't even want to think about them. Scum's too nice a word (I except the present publishers from that statement, of course).

I didn't want to think about them so much that once I started this chapter I turned my laptop off and went out. It was quite a nice day, for November. A bit misty, but mild. I had a walk in the park. Quite a lot of bird activity. I saw some sparrows, and a robin, and a couple of blue tits.

I still couldn't stop thinking about all the bastard publishers I'd ever had letters from, or hadn't had letters from when I should have, and the things they said. Like one letter I got, from some little twerp, after I'd sent in some brilliant idea, and he said, "This hasn't floated any boats round the office, I'm afraid."

Floated any boats. What sort of people are they? Aliens? Insects? Alien insects?

Anyway, to get away from remembering all those awful letters I went into town and walked round the shops.

There was no one I knew. I tried to remember where Kurt said he worked, because I wanted to have a word with him

A meeting of publishers *

about Diane. I had decided that no one was that lunatic, and he must have got mixed up between her and some other girl, though how you can get mixed up about the girl you went out with for two years, I don't know.

* *This is the thing about people who draw or paint. They take everything literally. I don't believe, Connolly, that the publishers were really playing around with boats. Hardly. They may be stupid, but in a meeting? Not very likely, is it?*
Unless he knows something I don't – after all, his brother-in-law's a publisher – and that's what they do. You know, make a paper boat out of the idea, and if it sinks reject it, and if it floats publish it. No. Surely they don't do that. But you never know with publishers. Just think, the stupidity of it. The ignorant superstition! All you have to do to get published is use stronger paper! To think that that might have been all that was between me and the Nobel Prize for Literature.

Anyway, I couldn't remember where he worked, so I went to the library and collected my e-mails. There were 34 trying to sell me Viagra, and 27 asking if I wanted a bigger penis. No, is the answer. I'll keep my own, thank you.

Nothing from anyone I knew.

I'm telling you all this not to fill up a chapter on a subject I refuse to write about, but to show you how lonely a writer's life can be, especially on a Tuesday morning in November.

It's something Laura never understood. When Adam was two, and Jordan a baby, and she was working in Quality Control at the pickle factory (a job that was, frankly, not the most stressful, unless you took the quality of pickles seriously) and I was desperately trying to sell **How To Write a Stinking Letter of Complaint**, she would actually question whether we were right to send the boys to a childminder.

"I mean, you're at home all day," she would say.

She never understood what it was like, waiting day after day for that letter to say, "We love your book, Mr Piddock, just sign here and the cheque will be with you by return of post."

And those waiting days weren't idle ones. I was busy thinking of my next oeuvre, but it was hard, I now had two works written and unpublished, as well as one planned but unwritten (thanks to the plagiarism of Ryan Jinks).

I didn't watch daytime TV in those days for fun, you know. My best thoughts often come to me while I'm watching mindless pap. And, while I had a huge number of truly inspirational ideas, I didn't want to begin the slog of planning them out until

---

FACT BOX 39

By the way, if you ever get accused of plagiarism (not anything that's ever happened to me, of course – more like the other way round) what you should say is: "I was inspired by your work." My personal cast iron guarantee the other person will be so flattered they'll go away purring. Another tip that on its own is worth the cover price. I spoil you all!

I was sure there was a good chance they'd be published this time.

And not long after that, all my time was filled following Laura to see when and where she was conducting her affair with Ryan.

I thought I knew why it had started, between her and him. Obviously it wasn't because he was better looking than me. And I had beaten him several times at squash, so he wasn't fitter. And he really hasn't much of a personality. Nor does he always have an opinion on everything. And I think everyone would agree with me that as far as writing is concerned, I'm streets ahead in every department. In fact I'm in the next city, as far as writing is concerned.

But he's luckier. And women like that.

chapter eighteen

The world wide web

The internet is symptomatic of all that is good and bad about modern technology.

On the one hand any information you want is out there, just a click on the computer and you can discover the most abstruse fact. But unfortunately, on the other, you'll never know if it's true or not.

It's like that old idea about monkeys typing at random, and if they did it forever they'd write Shakespeare's plays. Except you'd have to know Shakespeare's plays before you realised it was Shakespeare. And if you knew Shakespeare's plays there'd be no need for you to get the monkeys to type forever.

Well, there are a lot of monkeys out there, typing like fury, and there's very little Shakespeare being produced.

So you could, very easily, get your own website, and, after your How To Write Book has been rejected by the 100th publisher and 150th agent, put your book on your website, and there, in a sense, it's been published.

But who will know whether you're a monkey, or a Brian Piddock?

I spend a lot of time on the internet in the library, trying

FACT BOX 40

Most of the information I've put in the Fact Boxes of this book has been taken from the internet. However, I have scrupulously double checked them with several sources, especially knowledgeable friends of mine. Naturally I exclude Mad Mac from those, except that if he says something isn't true you know it must be.

to get information. Let's say I need to know who the Prime Minister of Australia is (because there was an argument down the pub, and there's a fiver resting on this). After an hour I know the best airfare from Heathrow to Sydney, the name of the straits between the mainland and Tasmania, the biggest computer shop in Adelaide, and Queensland's chief export, but I haven't found the name of the Prime Minister. After another hour, I arrive at the page of the Australian government, and they've got the name of their own Prime Minister wrong! I know it's Bob Hawke and has been for years, and I will tell Mad Mac it said so on the net and I was right and he was wrong, because I am and he is.

That's the trouble with the net.

You can put your book on the Web, but who will drink it?

Anyway, it gives me a headache, reading out lots of words on the screen, and if you put your book on the internet who's going to spend a fortune printing it out? And if they did they'd probably drop and scatter all 200 pages, and after they'd picked it up the whole thing'll read like a William Burroughs novel.

Forget the Web. You'll think you're the spider, but you're a helpless, hopeless fly.

Ryan Jinks was my fly, in the web I created to trap him.

I realised quite soon that it was no use trailing Laura. One day I followed at a discreet distance when she went to the pickle factory at 9 (she had been moved into the Personnel Department by then).

I parked my car on the opposite side of the road and sat, and waited, and watched, with only a newspaper and the radio to amuse me. And she didn't reappear until 5.30, when she got into her car, and drove home. I had to speed through town to get ahead of her and make it look as if I'd been working all day.

On Saturday she said she was going shopping, and I thought this was my chance to catch her, and I followed discreetly as she parked, went into Marks & Spencer, Selfridges, had a coffee, Laura Ashley, the hairdressers for two hours, John Lewis's, had another coffee, Dorothy Perkins, and came home.

Either she knew I was watching her, or they met at strange times, so I decided it would be better to watch Ryan than her.

He lives on the edge of town, almost in the country, a semi-detached house with trees at the bottom of the garden. Rather a nice house, actually. His parents left him the money to buy it, so I heard.

FACT BOX 41

R yan used to be married, to a fairly attractive woman called Marina. There was a lot of speculation in the pub as to why she left him, speculation which I'm not going to repeat or add to here. Suffice to say, I don't believe the rumour about the Thai lapdancer. Mercifully, he and his former wife had no children.

I found that if I parked my car on Huston Street, and walked along a disused railway track, and across a field, I could arrive behind the street that Ryan's house was on. I then had to crawl behind the hedges at the bottom of the gardens, until I was behind a little group of ash trees, and, standing carefully, I could peer over a branch and looked straight into the study where Ryan "worked".

He was about 20 yards away, but I found with binoculars I could fix on his face through the window as he sat by his desk, and with no fear that he could see me, so long as I kept very still.

It was not an edifying sight, as he picked his nose, reached down to scratch himself, chewed on his pencil, and rotated his scrawny neck. I couldn't quite see, but I could imagine, his little earring flapping as he moved his head.

Occasionally he bent down to write something. He worked by longhand, I noticed. It amused me to think that he didn't trust computers any more, after his failure to back up the work for his last book.

I did find the experience fascinating, in a repulsive sort of way, and I recommend to any How To Write writer to find some third-rate hack and, if you can hold your stomach down, study him attempting to work, preferably without him knowing it.

You notice things. I'd never realised how Ryan's mouth could open in such a slack-jawed way as he stared into space. Or how often he pulled at his beard. It was a wonder he had any of it left. Or how he ate the ends of his moustache, probably for the food he'd left there from yesterday's dinner.

I never tired of it. I spent a week, just standing and watching him, from when Laura left in the morning until she came home, allowing for the time it took me to get there and back.

I used to take sandwiches and coffee, and a little seat. I was perfectly well hidden, if I ducked down behind the trees.

What I liked most, I think, was seeing the struggle he had with words. The way he would bend down as if this was it, he had a whole chapter just eager to pour out, and after a few seconds, when he could only have written half a dozen words, he'd stop, look up again, rest his forehead in his hand, and stare out of the window.

I freely admit I could have spent months there, it was such an education, but I thought I ought to get back to my latest work.

And besides, one day when I was sitting on my little camp chair and sipping a coffee, there was a noise to my left and a voice saying, "Brian?"

I jumped up, spilling the warm coffee on my trousers. It was Ryan, leaning over the garden fence.

This was a tricky moment.

"Hi, Ryan," I said, recomposing my cool with admirable agility.

"What are you doing?" he said.

"Oh. Just a bit of birdwatching."

"At the back of my garden?"

"Yes. It's an excellent spot." I indicated the rather barren field in front of us. I couldn't at that moment see a single bloody bird. "Usually. You get all sorts. Crows. Starlings. A rusty throated wren babbler. I just saw one of those."

"Then why are your binoculars pointing into my house?"

"I'm just resting them there, that's all. Is there a problem with that?" I said, quite aggressively. It's very important to turn defence into attack as soon as you can.

"One of my neighbours has been watching you from her bathroom. She said you've been here for days now, pointing your binoculars into my house."

"Only because I saw a bird fly into your garden. A tit. A great tit. I rather like great tits." I folded my chair and picked it up, and took my binoculars. "But I'm sorry I seem to have offended you. I didn't realise birdwatching was allowed everywhere except within half a mile of your house."

I stomped off before he could reply. I'd forgotten my sandwiches, but that was a small price. I thought I'd handled it very well. The important thing was not to change my story in any way. In fact, I almost believed it myself, except I've never had an interest in birds. But Ryan wasn't to know that.

Nuisance about the neighbour, though. I had got complacent, that was the trouble. It meant I couldn't really continue to watch Ryan, because I didn't think I could so easily talk myself out of it the second time, and if he saw me again he might start to suspect I knew something.

In conclusion, putting your book on the internet takes about 15 minutes of time, and it's time well wasted. Truth is a precious commodity, but what value does it have if it is indistinguishable from a lie?

Mind you, I wish someone would tell me in plain English how you can get your own website and how you then create a web page. But computer geeks don't seem to have an affinity with plain English, preferring obfuscation.

Also, in conclusion, I saw Kurt yesterday. He was in Smith's, looking at the greetings cards.

I was careful to seem quite cheerful with him, in case he has a dangerous psychosis. Lucky I was. All I said was that I'd found out that Diane lived in Melbourne, not Edinburgh, and he almost screamed:

"I **** ****** know, you ******* ***** *** **** *******!"

A rusty throated wren babbler *

Right in the middle of WH Smith's.

That is not rational behaviour. I just backed away, slowly, keeping my eyes on him in case he moved to attack, and left the shop.

I thought about telling the police about him, but in my present circumstances it might not go down very well.

There are a lot of people I know who ought, by rights, to be having treatment in a secure hospital. And Kurt is a social worker, for goodness sake! Or, at least, he said he is. If true, it makes me fear for all the old people and children and other disadvantaged and disabled members of society. Perhaps he's a social worker in the same way as Mad Mac is Albert Einstein.

---

* *At last he's drawn something properly. Yes, that is exactly what a rusty throated wren babbler looks like, and that's exactly what I was looking for that day, at the back of Ryan's house. So do you believe me now, Ryan? Yes. Good. So who's got the last laugh, hmm?*

chapter nineteen

Self-publishing

O f course I do have this guilt, that it was my actions that took Kurt over the edge, when he split up with Diane. Though thank God he did, when you think what violence lurks under the surface. Because she was such a gentle person.

God knows why she's living in Australia. I wouldn't live in Australia if you transported me there.

Anyway, **Self-Publishing**. I have tried this, with my second work, *How To Write an Erotic Romantic Short Story*, and it didn't work.

Australia's full of Australians, for one thing.

It has been pointed out to me, by no less an authority than Ryan Jinks, and you can get no less of an authority than him, that *How To Write an Erotic Romantic Short Story* was vanity published, and not self-published.

This is nonsense. If there is a difference, I don't know what it is.

What I particularly dislike about Australians is their horrible misuse of the English language. Worse than computer geeks. Worse, even, than journalists. Worse, believe or not, than that lack-of-style guru Ryan Jinks.

Look, there's nothing vainer than publishing your book yourself. All you're doing is saying, "Look at me, I've got my name on the front cover of this book."

Actually, when you think about it, all publishing is vanity. You're just jumping up and down trying to attract everyone's attention. Attention seeking, that's all it is. Like a little child.

I think I realised this most forcefully one night in the Golden Lion, not long after my attempt at getting *How To Write a Stinking Letter of Complaint* published, and letting

Jack the Hack look at it, and his being so singularly unhelpful
and pedantically critical.

In fact I was discussing Jack with Rowdy Pete. Discussing
isn't quite the word, Rowdy Pete scarcely says anything more
than Yes or No or Cheers. Maybe an All right, or an Okay. So I
was probably talking rather more than he was, deploring Jack's
lack of linguistic ability, his imperception, and his insensitivity.
The kind of thing one friend can say to another about a third.

FACT BOX 42

Australians say, " speccy", instead of "spectacular". I met
one, in the Lake District, and he said, "There's some
really good speccy views up ahead."
What would it have cost him to say "spectacular views"?
He saved himself two syllables, and lost his soul in the
process.
Then he offered me some chewies and chokkie, and com-
plained that his trackies were wet. It was lucky he was bigger than me, or I'd have pushed him off the mountain.
Mountie, I mean, of course.
What a country.

The main point I made was how Jack and all the others
couldn't possibly understand what it was like to be a professional author, as they'd never written a book.

That was when Pete said, "Actually, I've written a novel."

I don't know if I can convey to you the effect of this.
Imagine if a politician had said, "Actually, I'm telling the
truth." Or a publisher had said, "Actually, I have a great respect
for writers."

What would you think? You wouldn't believe them, would
you? Except Rowdy Pete isn't a politician or a publisher, he's an
honest sort of bloke. Which could only mean that, even though
Rowdy Pete is not the kind of person who seems to have much
sense of humour, this was a joke.

I started laughing in a sardonic that-isn't-very-funny I'm-being-serious way.

"Really," he said. "It's got about 100,000 words. It's about my experiences in the Forestry Commission. I've been thinking about trying to get it published, but I didn't know where to start. I thought you might have a look at it, or give me some advice, seeing as how you've had something in print."

I didn't answer. I couldn't. I supposed I had to believe him. Rowdy Pete had written a novel of 100,000 words. This was a man who I'd only heard speak about a hundred words since I'd met him, 15 years ago, and I'd seen him at least twice a week, every week, in the pub.

I just muttered something about how I'd love to see it, sometime, and I turned to watch the match on the screen.

It was only a few days later I mentioned this to Dan the Van, what a dark horse Pete was, and well done to him, of course, but he still couldn't appreciate what it was like being a professional writer, and the pain of sending things off and having to wait for a decision, and the bloody publishers are never quite sure.

"Does that mean my screenplay counts?" said Dan. "Because DreamWorks seemed quite interested in it, if I trimmed it a bit, and then I trimmed it but they decided against it. I sent it to Zenith instead."

I stared at him. "Your screenplay?"

"It's about my time in the Territorial Army, when I was sent to Belize. It was such a great experience, in the jungle."

I nodded, and went to the bar. Mad Mac was chatting to the barmaid. I told him what Dan had said.

"That's just not a very good joke," I said.

"It's not a joke. I've seen it. It's not bad. He asked me where he could send it."

"He asked you?"

"Because I'd mentioned my sitcom. About the removals firm. I'd sent it to the BBC. They said it was too rude, but Channel 4 might be interested."

That was the moment I let slip a swear word. Loudly. I had

been pushed too far. Either they were taking the piss, had got together and decided to wind me up, or the world had gone mad. Either way, I wasn't amused. Not in the slightest. I take my job seriously, and it was hard enough without having those plonkers deride me in that way.

The whole pub went quiet. Frank The Ape came over.

"What's going on?" he said.

Frank's a joker. Always good for a laugh. If he sees me, he always say, "Ah, here's Mr Pillock", which is extremely amusing, the first time. And when Ryan Jinks used to come in the pub, he'd say, " Jinx! Now you can't speak," which was a lot wittier, even after 50 times.

"Brian doesn't seem to like the fact that some of us have written things," said Dan.

"That's not what I said!"

Frank stood, with his pint. I thought, Well, at least he'll defuse the situation with a little joke or other, even if it isn't very funny.

"Well," he said, "when I wrote my book about my early childhood, and how my dad used to hit me, and I had to deliver milk to pay for my own school dinners, I found that quite painful. It was hard. But I have to say it was worth it. Dan had a look at it, didn't you? And you thought it was all right. You thought it might be worth sending it off, didn't you? I might do that. Would you like to have a look at it, Brian?"

I didn't reply. I finished what was left of my pint, and I left them standing there, and I walked home, a lonely walk past snogging couples and drunken youths. I couldn't speak to Laura, but went straight to my study, and I looked at **How To Write a Stinking Letter of Complaint**, and I was tempted to put it straight in the dustbin.

This is what it had come to, my life as a writer. I should end it all, the pain, the sorrow, the regret. And I began to compose, in my head, a few words I could leave on my desk. About the betrayals, from friends, colleagues, family, and every other person in the world.

They were a very good few words. They had pith, and feeling, and a touch of wit. I got rather excited. I scribbled a few ideas down on a piece of paper. It looked good.

And two months later — no exaggeration — after the easiest and most joyful writing I've ever done, I had the rough outline of:

How To Write a Suicide Note.

It is, and I know you'd agree if you could only get the chance to look at it, written with clarity and verve. It's the first, and last, word on the subject. And what's so important, it's one of the most useful How To Write Books ever written. Because so many people just don't have the vocabulary or prose to put their feelings on paper, and if they get it wrong at this, the most crucial moment, then they'll never get another chance, and you can't say that about any other writing opportunity.

Because that note is going to be pored over like no other words you'll ever write. A hint of ambiguity, and the weight of accusation falls on the wrong person. Or, worse, it falls on no one at all!

But, amazingly, and so upsetting for me, so crushing, no publisher was interested in the treatment of the idea. I sent out a concise précis, plus a sample page, to 30 publishers, and not one responded positively. I was crushed. I was in despair. All those words that get printed by the spoilt children of the writing business or by the egregious dilettantes such as my "friends" down the Golden Lion, and my lovely and necessary work wasn't being seen by anyone, and it was so unfair. I felt like ending it all!

Then the answer occurred to me, as I sat one night, alone, at the bar of the Royal Oak, trying to get away from everyone I knew. Now I'm not one who approves of publicity stunts, but this was different. It wasn't really a stunt at all. I meant this.

I *would* kill myself. And as a suicide note I would leave:

How To Write a Suicide Note.

It was brilliant. For the first time in months I forgot that Laura and Ryan were having an affair, that my children ignored me, that my friends betrayed me, and I couldn't get any of my excellent work published. I felt great!

I just had to think of how to do it. I'm rather averse to pain, so I didn't want to hang myself, or jump off a cliff, or anything similar, but I wanted to make a large gesture. And, most importantly, I wanted **How To Write a Suicide Note** to be at the crux of the gesture. Also, I needed to make it clear that although all the publishers and agents of the world were partly to blame for my needless death, it was Laura and Ryan — especially Ryan — who was most responsible.

I set about planning and thinking it through as if I were about to write **How To Write War and Peace**.

Much better than self-publishing. I was going to *publish myself!*

Anyway, if you want to try self-publishing, it's fairly easy. Just find a printer, look in the Yellow Pages, give them a copy of your work on disk and a cheque for £4000, and in a little while you can fill your garage with all those lovely copies of your book.

And remember, you've cut out the middleman, so with every copy you sell the profit goes to you and no one else. Once you've paid off that £4000, of course. And how long is that going to take, at £11.99 a copy? 333.6 copies, that's all! You can't lose! You probably know 333.6 people, if you include people in your local, everyone in your street and the next few streets, everyone at work including the tea lady and cleaners, cousins, uncles, people who share your name, and so on, though whether they're generous enough to spend £11.99 on your book is another matter. I doubt if I know 0.6 people generous enough. Well it's not generosity, they're receiving valuable advice, and a book that any shelf would be proud to have.

You'll probably have to buy some advertising, or get a website where you can sell copies, and the technicalities of that are probably beyond even my eight-year-old son, who knows everything about computers.

You'll have to go around bookshops, too, and that's a

humiliating business, I can tell you. I tried it with *How To Write an Erotic Romantic Short Story*. Smith's and Waterstones will tell you everything is bought centrally and you have to be on the list, even if you point out to them that you're a local author, and bound to shift a lot of copies for that reason alone.

I could have hit that manager of Smith's. About 20, he was. Still had spots.

So you might end up putting half a dozen books into the tiny independent bookshop run by an old woman as a hobby (or possibly a front for a drug dealing operation), on a sale or return basis, and go back in six months to be told they'd had no sale and it was all return.

It's heartbreaking. You end up giving them away as Christmas presents, and you have to suffer the look of disappointment and the insincere thank yous of the recipients.

But let me not put you off. Give it a go, if you've got the money, stamina, and luck, and if you succeed, tell me how you did it, because I think it's bloody impossible. Of course Stephen King tried it and it worked for him, but he didn't need to do it.

That's an idea. self-publish under the name Stephen King. You can always say, in little writing in the inside front cover, "Not *that* Stephen King."

Otherwise, do it my way. Think of the best publicity stunt you can. Get your **How To Write Publicity for a Publicity Stunt** printed, and then blow up the Houses of Parliament, and I guarantee you won't have printed enough copies, they'll be selling so fast. Unless some po-faced Home Secretary (the replacement for the one that was killed in the blast) bans your work on the grounds it's the proceeds of criminal activity.

For my *How To Write a Suicide Note* I didn't decide to blow up the Houses of Parliament. I didn't know where to get enough gunpowder, and I reckoned that security had probably been tightened up since 1603. I didn't even decide to blow up the Bloomsbury area of London, where a lot of publishers and agents have their offices, because I didn't really want to cause the deaths of several hundred thousand people, some of which were probably quite innocent of crimes against me.

Instead, I decided to go to Ryan Jinks' home, and blow it and myself up.

What a great way to go. I wasn't even bothered whether Ryan was in the house or not at that time, he'd be so upset that his computer and his handwritten manuscript were destroyed he'd wished he had been in the house at the time and blown up.

Parliament, after Piddock's visited *

* *I could have done it. Blown it up, I mean. I wish I had, now. All right, I would have deplored the loss of life and all that. Except it would only have been politicians and civil servants. But I didn't. And what is my reward for sticking to the exact letter of the law and not reducing Parliament to a pile of debris? To be scorned and mistreated, that's what.*

And in the aftermath, as everyone was saying, "Why did he do it? He had so much promise. He was unlucky, true, but had such ability. He was easily the finest How To Write writer of his or any other generation, if only the fickle world had realised it," there'd be a single post-it note on my computer screen at home (probably fixed with Sellotape, post-it notes can lose their stickiness on glass, and it would have been a disaster if it had fallen off and gone behind the desk where no one could see it) saying, simply:

"Look on the C drive, under *My Documents*. Under the *Books* folder. In *Latest Work*. ***howtowriteasuicidenote.doc***."

And they'd read it, and realise how blind and foolish they'd been, and Laura would refuse ever to see Ryan again, and Ryan would creep off to some hole and never be so arrogant again as to dare to try and write a word, and there would be a million pound publishing auction for ***How To Write a Suicide Note***, finally won by my old publishers, Crocker & Thistle, the ones who published ***How To Write a Novel About Modern Working-Class Life***, and there would be an inquiry as to how they'd let me slip through their fingers, the result of which would mean the sacking of half their staff.

How To Write a Suicide Note would be a bestseller, the best How To Write Book bestseller that ever sold best. There would only be one How To Write writer. I would be the Roger Federer or Ellen MacArthur or Steve Redgrave of How To Write Books. Even though I'd set up in my will half the royalties to start a fund for Destitute and Undiscovered How To Write writers, there would still be enough money coming in for Laura to give up work in the pickle factory and send the boys to public school.

It was a marvellous plan, and I knew it would work. All people have to do is dress up as Batman or Spiderman to get loads of publicity. This was a million times more imaginative. It was a winner. I've never been more sure of anything.

There was only one problem. It was such a good plan, so bound to work and make me at last successful, famous and rich, that I didn't want to die any more.

It was the last thing I was going to do! Blow myself up? Not a chance. I wanted to enjoy my success, fame and wealth.

This was tricky. How, I wondered, could I commit suicide without killing myself?

That little problem was all that delayed me, and as it turned out, that was a fatal delay to my well wrought plans.

Because in that little intervening period while I was looking for the final piece to fit into the jigsaw of my brilliant plan, I fell in love.

In conclusion, if you publish your own books you can always advertise your other books in the books you publish yourself, so long as you sell any of them in the first place.

I've still got loads of **How To Write an Erotic Romantic Short Story**, price £9.99 including post and package. It's a damn good read, even if I say so myself.

And, of course, you can always say so if you publish it yourself. Put it on the front cover:

"A Damn Good Read!" — Stephen King.

No one's going to know about your imaginary mate called King, first name Steve.

Though don't do that if you're going to assume the name "Stephen King" as the author, or it won't look quite so good.

chapter twenty

Unusual ways of publishing

Interesting topic. I don't know any Unusual Ways of Publishing. I've already covered publishing on the Web, but as I said even if I knew how to do it I don't believe anyone would read it on a screen, and certainly not print it out.

Otherwise, what is there? Printing it on toilet paper so people can read it while they're sitting on the loo? Difficult to gauge the correct ratio of words to paper. I mean some heavy users of toilet paper might not sit there long enough and would flush half the chapter. Laura's like that. She folds over the paper and uses double thickness. It's such a waste.

I don't know, either, whether you can print on toilet paper, though now I think about it ***How To Write an Erotic Romantic Short Story*** was printed on paper that was of lesser quality than toilet paper, so maybe it is possible.

But do you really want the words you have struggled with so long and love so much end up abused in that fashion? I don't think so.

There was an idea I read about a while ago to shine a picture on the moon, and I suppose you could put some words up there, but unless you had a pretty good telescope I can't see it working with a book. A page at a time might be all right, but you'd always get the fast reader saying, "I'm finished, turn over," and the slow one saying, "Hang on, I'm only halfway down."

I always think those people in Oxford Street who hold up boards advertising Golf Sales could be better utilised, so you could have two or three paragraphs a sign, if each board was about 15 yards apart, so managed carefully with a whole series of people, the average walker could read almost a whole chapter between Marble Arch and Tottenham Court Road.

It would increase the number of people who bump into each other, which would be a distraction, and you might lose your place, and when do you arrange to show the next chapter? The next day, but your reader might not walk along Oxford Street the next day. The next week, but he or she might have got annoyed they'd had to read the same chapter five times, or seven if they worked at weekends.

Mobile phone text messaging has certainly not fulfilled its potential, and I can definitely see a market for the canny publisher who arranges to send out a book as a long text message.

But, I'm sorry, I refuse to have my work rendered as:

Hw t wrt txt mssg by brn pdck

FACT BOX 43

I suspect Australians must be behind text messaging, with their addiction to abbreviating.
Brizzie, there's another one, short for Brisbane. Mackers for McDonald's, and sunnies for sunglasses. What with Murdoch and all it makes me wonder if Australians are intent on taking over all the media in the world, and will then make abbreving complsry.

Well that's not bad. Four strong ideas for the How To Write writer willing to take a bit of a risk:

1   **Cloakroom Utility Propagation**
2   **Lunar Narrowcasting**
3   **Serial Placard Publication**
4   **Mobile Phone Messaging**

It's good to see I've still got my imaginative faculties intact, despite the traffic on this main road, the headache I've got, and a bit of a cold.

I think you've got your money's worth there, so I'll just finish the chapter by telling you about Holly.

It's amazing how your life can go on as mine did then,

trailing Laura and staking out Ryan's house to get proof of their affair, and planning to blow myself up to get my latest work published, and suddenly all that ordinary and predictable routine changes with one chance meeting.

Holly was the beautiful ex-girlfriend of my nephew Jason, and for a couple of years I used to think of her, fondly. In fact I mentioned her to my sister, Jason's mum.

"Oh yes, we keep in touch," she said. "She lives in Birmingham now."

Well that was a coincidence, as Birmingham is only an hour's drive from here, except when the traffic's busy, and on the train I have to go through Birmingham if I'm on the way to, say, Derby. And as a further coincidence, Christmas was coming up, and Birmingham has much better shops than here, so I thought I might pop in one day.

Holly worked in an art gallery, so Sally told me. Obviously I didn't go looking for her, I had no intentions that way of any kind. I mean, I knew she was startlingly beautiful, but I was a married man with two children, even if my wife was messing around with another man.

But as it happened, after a couple of hours with my Birmingham A-Z, I did find myself walking past the gallery, and I thought I might as well pop in and see how she was.

It was a Modern Art art gallery, you know the sort, installations, piles of junk that someone's dragged off a skip and welded together and charged a fortune. I couldn't see Holly anywhere, but I was standing in front of one of those monstrosities when a girl who seemed to work there walked into the room.

"This is fascinating," I said to her, as a way of talking to her.

"Isn't it?" she said. She was rather plain, with glasses, her hair in a bun.

"Some people seem to think this sort of thing is just a conversation piece, but I think it's much more than that," I said, to keep the conversation going.

"Oh yes."

I turned to her.

"Actually," I said, "you must know Holly. Holly Bracknell."

Conversation piece *

"Oh yes. Holly? Oh yes. She works here."
"That's what I thought."
I waited for this rather gormless girl to tell me where Holly
was. It took a few seconds.

---

* *This is nothing like what was in that gallery. It was a sculpture we were looking at, for
a start. You know, I think this is some doodle Connolly had and he didn't know what to do
with it so he just bunged it off. I mean what if I worked like that, and just wrote whatever
came into my head and put down any kind of irrelevance whenever I felt like it, like for
instance that I was planning to have beans on two pieces of toast for my tea tonight? No
one would put up with it. Luckily I'm disciplined, that's all I can say.*

"Oh! But she's not here now. She doesn't work Tuesday mornings."

"Ah."

"Though you've only got an hour and a half to wait, before she'll be in."

"Well she's a very dear friend, but I'd only see her if she happened to be around. Though I think I will have a cup of coffee in your cafe. I don't suppose you would care to join me?"

"Oh. I can't just yet. My lunch break isn't for half an hour."

"I can wait half an hour. I still have several rooms to see first."

I had been conceiving a plan. Always turn adversity into an advantage, as Napoleon once said. It would be an idea if I found out more about Holly before I saw her, in order not to make some embarrassing faux pas.

Abbie, that was the mousy girl's name, was a fount of knowledge about Holly. Holly didn't have a boyfriend at present, was indeed rather lonely and friendless. I could have kissed Abbie, despite her unattractive persona. It all sounded very promising.

I told Abbie about my career, and she seemed very impressed, kept trying to interrupt me to tell me how much she admired writers and all their work, but I expected it was because she hadn't been around writers much, as I have. I am all too aware of their frailties, unfortunately.

It was at this point that Holly entered the café. She was still stunning, tall and elegant, her hair pulled back in a severe way off her face that emphasised the beauty of her eyes. I recognised her immediately, even after three years.

Unfortunately, she didn't recognise me. But why should she, she wasn't expecting to see me? I didn't allow it to embarrass me in front of Abbie, but simply reminded Holly of who I was. I think she remembered me then.

"He's a writer," said Abbie.

I smiled suavely, I was about to show a little modesty, and diminish my talents, though not too much, when Abbie turned to me:

"So's Holly. I was trying to say. She's just had her first novel published. It's been longlisted for the Booker Prize. Isn't that fantastic?"

I expect I agreed, that it was indeed fantastic, though I don't really remember. I only remember wanting to get out of that place as soon as possible, because I did have a lot of shopping to do, and as I looked at Holly I realised her beauty was of the model type, rather superficial, and frankly, skin deep. The sort that would look good on the back of a book cover, and appeal to some horny hoary old Booker Prize judge who thought he could make a conquest by voting for her.

Abbie walked with me to the entrance. I don't even remember saying goodbye to Holly.

Abbie was talking, something about it being her afternoon off, and she could go now but she wasn't sure what to do. I suggested, since I had nothing better to do, and needed something to take my mind off my troubles, that we go and see a film.

We watched some French thing at an independent cinema, and then had a pizza at some Italian place. I must admit, I wasn't really listening much to what Abbie said, I suppose I was thinking what a cruel deception it was, that beautiful women like Holly could turn out to be such shallow, shallow people.

We went for a drink, and somehow, I'm not sure how or when, ended up in Abbie's little flat in Ladywood. I realised I had missed the last train home, and rang Laura to tell her I was going to sleep on the settee of a friend, and that was what I fully intended to do, except to be quite honest — and I had had one or two drinks — when Abbie took off her glasses, and unpinned her hair, she didn't look that bad. And she did reveal rather unexpected talents in bed.

In fact, in the morning, I concluded that it had been an extremely satisfactory few hours. The fact was that if I had graced Holly with the attention I had lavished on Abbie she wouldn't have been especially grateful, being, I saw now, one of those rather self-centred girls who think the world revolves around them. And while I might have been rather self-conscious with her, because at 45 I'm aware that I'm not as fit as I was at 23, and I apparently snore a little, since Abbie wasn't that attractive it didn't really matter what I was like.

I felt no guilt, either, because what Laura and Ryan had been getting up to — if only I could prove it — was a far worse betrayal than anything I might do.

It surprised me rather, though, that as I was leaving Abbie's flat she asked me when she could see me again. I was about to begin my usual well-rehearsed speech from when I was a student, I'd have to see, it might be difficult, I hardly ever come this way, I was going abroad for three years, I was going on a trip up an unclimbed Andean mountain and probably wouldn't make it back — you know, the usual thing — when I realised I wouldn't mind seeing Little Miss Abbie again, and I told her I'd take her phone number and see. Though she was on no account to ring me.

I had to endure the usual jealous rages when I got home, who was the friend whose settee I'd slept on, what had I got up to, and so on.

I told Laura she was living in a fantasy world, which of course she was, though she did shake me rather when she said she was aware that Holly Bracknell lived and worked in Birmingham. I feigned ignorance of who Holly was, and we had the usual awful row about how she knew I fancied Holly, and I protested that she had no interest for me. And it was so unfair because she hadn't. Laura just couldn't face the truth, that was the trouble, and she still can't, because I was entirely innocent of her accusations.

Blogging, there's another Unusual Way of Publishing. I'm not entirely clear what blogging is. Something to do with the internet. I suspect it's just another means of telling everyone what you think. There are too many people already who think we're going to be interested in what they think, we don't want to give them another way of doing it. Not that anyone'll read it, that's one thing.

5   Blogging

That's five good suggestions I've given you. I'm not past it yet. Rumours of my demise as an imaginative and helpful How To Write writer are wildly exaggerated.

The point about Holly and Abbie was that I was really doing some research for *How To Write a Suicide Note*. That book had changed and developed as I wrote it. While at the planning stage it was merely a manual to assist those in need of putting their last thoughts on paper, with some handy examples to make life easier, I found I was going back to it in order to expand the whole concept, until it almost became (though I usually deplore the genre) a self-help book.

How To Write a Suicide Note isn't just about getting your last words right. It's about getting your last moments right. In my case, once I decided on blowing myself and Ryan Jinks' house up, I felt there were one or two things I needed to do first, and making love to a young and beautiful woman was certainly number one. All right, Abbie wasn't beautiful, not by any means, and she was in her late 20s, but that wasn't bad for someone like me who was at an age when other men are almost middle-aged and past it.

The trouble was, the writing for *How To Write a Suicide Note* was proceeding wonderfully, the best I'd ever known, it was two-thirds completed, I was finding new ideas, I kept adding to earlier chapters, I was full of energy and life, that I now felt even less like killing myself.

Rewriting, even when you think the work is all finished and wrapped up, is extremely important. In a sense, no work is ever finished. It's part of the craft of being a How To Write writer, the moulding, the redrafting, the constant striving for perfection.

But I've already made this point, earlier in this book, in the chapter on **Redrafting**, if you'd care to read it.

Ah. Now I look I see I don't have a chapter on redrafting. Right.

chapter twenty-one

Redrafting

I enjoy redrafting probably more than anything else. You've done the hard work, you've got a working manuscript, all you need to do now is correct a few spelling mistakes, put things in the right order, and expand the sections that need expanding.

It can be very satisfying. Take the sentence, "Make sure you make others suffer as they've made you suffer" (from *How To Write a Suicide Note*, chapter 7, page 61). I pondered, and wondered whether there were too many not very pretty mades in a row there? I changed "Make sure" to "Be certain", and "make others" to "get others". Then I realised "suffer" wasn't harsh enough, I preferred "torture", and "others" was a little imprecise, so I was more specific, until I had: "Be certain you get your wife and colleague tortured as they've made you be tortured."

And a very pleasant afternoon had passed. The next day I may have looked at it again and thought that, on balance, version one was better. It's all part of the creative process, in the same way as was my night with Abbie.

Now many other How To Write writers would have simply ticked off Abbie as a mission accomplished, and be heartless enough never to have rung her again, fearing the millstone round their necks of the loveless and lonely girl desperate for affection.

Not me. I'm not made like that.

I left it a couple of months, because it was a very busy time for me. I realised there were a lot of other things I desperately wanted to do in my life, and I think I was quite right not to let anything get in my way of doing them. I owed it to myself, and the world of literature.

But Laura and I weren't getting on at all well — not surprisingly, the time she was spending with Ryan, though I hadn't quite managed to find out when that was.

So I thought it would be rather pleasant for Abbie if I paid her another visit.

I rang her at her flat. She sounded quite surprised to hear from me. She said it had been a long time since she had seen me. I began to tell her about all the vital work I was doing, redrafting my book, when she interrupted me, and told me she was seeing someone else.

I must admit, I don't like that expression.

"Well you can see me as well, can't you?" I said, without, I think, showing my annoyance.

"No, I'm afraid not, Brian. He's my boyfriend. We're going out together."

We talked a little more. I did get a little heated, I must admit. I told her that I'd built my hopes and dreams around her — a slight exaggeration, but accurate in a metaphorical sense — and she was trying to destroy me as a creative artist.

"But you didn't ring," she said.

"You didn't ring me!"

"You didn't give me your phone number!"

"Of course I didn't," I said. "I'm a married man with two children!"

Her tone rather changed at that point. She claimed I hadn't told her I was married and with children. Well, we hadn't spent that long together. I didn't have time to tell her my life story.

Anyway, the upshot was she refused to see me again.

I was bitterly hurt, I don't mind admitting it. I had been so close to killing myself, and had dragged myself out of the mire of despair by sheer willpower, and she was pushing me right back into the quicksand.

Worse, I felt so bad, I found I couldn't work, even though I knew How To Write a Suicide Note was very close to becoming the perfect How To Write Book, if I could have only spent a couple of clear weeks on it.

But artistic temperament can't be forced.

I had loved that girl, and she treated me like this.

I wanted to kill myself. I would kill myself. I would finish **How To Write a Suicide Note** as my lasting legacy.

I had made my decision, and I would stick to it.

The trouble was, I couldn't finish **How To Write a Suicide Note** because I was in a suicidal despair.

This was getting annoying. First I couldn't kill myself because I was feeling good about my book. Now I couldn't kill myself because I was in such a suicidal mood I couldn't finish my book.

I've made a flow chart to make this clearer. I wish I had this at the time, because it might have made decision-making a lot easier, but I was feeling too bad:

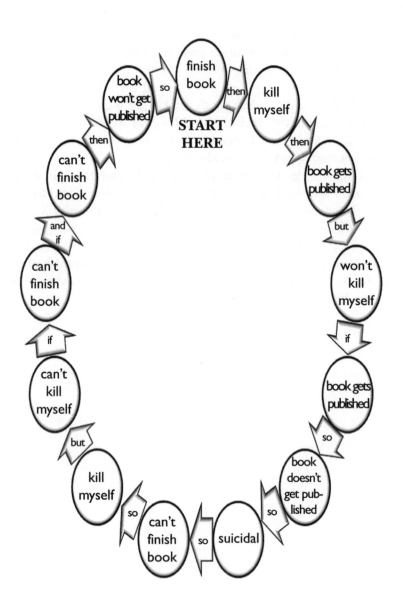

Just follow this flow chart for ten minutes, and you'll begin
to comprehend the depths I was in.

chapter twenty-two

Payment

I t's a wonderful thing to be paid for what you enjoy doing, and as How To Write writers we are privileged, because so many people in modern society don't enjoy what they do, and only live for the weekends when they can go to the pub and watch sport on TV. While I can go to the pub and watch sport on TV every day of the week!

But getting that cheque through the post for your artistic endeavour is more than just money, more than just a wage slip.

It's the way society has for thanking you for what you do.

I remember my advance for **How To Write a Novel About Modern Working-Class Life**. It wasn't huge. It didn't even get near four figures. But after that letter dropped through the box and I opened it and took out its contents, I treasured that cheque for the whole half-hour it took me to get into town and put it in my bank account and get the money out so I could go to the pub.

It's a wonderful feeling, and while we can't all be JK Rowlings and feel like we've won the rollover prize at the lottery every week, it's almost as good.

Until you add up the work in hours you've put in and discover you're being paid less than a Lancashire mill worker circa 1819, not allowing for inflation.

I once added up all the money I'd earned through writing, and compared it with the money Laura had earned in the same time, in the pickle factory (and this was well before she became Managing Director).

I had earned 0.98% of what she had earned. She had earned 10,204.081% of what I had earned. In a pickle factory!

I don't need to point out to you that there must be

something very wrong with a society that treats its finest artists like this.

Of course, no doubt, if I'd been a brainless supermodel who had scribbled a few garbled thoughts onto her shopping list, the figures would be reversed.

Modern life is sick, there's no question. People like me are the ones who lay the golden eggs, and who gets the takings? Publishers, agents, booksellers, footballers, and supermodels.

Money, or the lack of it, was what finally pushed me over the edge. It wasn't that my wife was betraying me with my colleague. It wasn't my sons refusing to play footie with me on the lawn because they said I was crap. It wasn't even that the girl I had loved and cherished had kneed me in the testicles (metaphorically, I mean).

It was debt.

Well, doing those last few things everyone should do in their life proved to be bloody expensive. Having a bottle of 1999 Chateau Lafitte Rothschild. You wouldn't believe how much that was, and I'm not sure I enjoyed it as much as a bottle of £3.99 vin de pays d'Oc. Though I did eat a curry with it so I suppose my taste buds weren't at their most attuned.

Visiting a lap dancing club in London. That was very expensive.

Drinking the finest malt whisky there is. Well, the most expensive, anyway. I did enjoy that, though I probably shouldn't have drunk the whole bottle in one sitting, on my own.

These are all things I felt obliged, as an artist, to do, and yet they brought me, because of the way our sick modern society treats its artists, to near bankruptcy.

It didn't matter. While I had drunk the whisky I had been inspired enough to make out a plan:

1 Finish **How To Write a Suicide Note**.
2 Go to Ryan's house and blow it up, with me inside.
3 Get **How To Write a Suicide Note** published.
4 Make enough money to pay off all my debts.
5 With some of that money, get enough dynamite to blow

up Ryan's house.

6 Feel good enough about myself having done all that to complete 1.

7 Feel bad enough about myself to do 2.

Piddock at work *

I read this once I'd recovered enough from my hangover, about a week later. It certainly was a plan, and in its own way it was a good plan, but I did feel its time-challenging structure was more suited to a High Concept Science-Fiction novel than

---

* *Now wait a minute. I'm not going to take this sort of thing from anyone. This is Connolly's last warning. One more insulting drawing like this and I shall ring the publishers and demand they get another person to do the pictures.*

reality.

I ripped up my plan, got in the car, and drove over to Ryan's house. Never mind plans and flow charts. It was time to make a Big Gesture.

Anyway, don't let me put you off. Some people make a lot of money from writing. Maybe 14 or 15, in the whole world. And they make so much money they don't know what to do with it, except to buy another luxury mansion in another country. Couldn't they share it out with the rest of us? Oh no. Thank you, Grisham. Thank you, Brown, D.

It makes you want to be a socialist. Almost.

FACT BOX 44

By the way, unless you do win the lottery JK Rowling-style, don't bother to get an accountant. Just make up some figure for expenses on your tax return. They'll never check.

I shouldn't be telling you this. It's probably the next thing that will happen to me. I'll get descended on by a wolf pack from the Inland Revenue: "Let's see your receipts for the last 30 years."

As the saying goes, when you're so far down the only way is not up, there's always a bit further down.

Unless, as some stupid bloody Sunday newspaper colour magazine would say, "Down is the new up."

There are even some people who make a lot of money from writing How To Write Books.

It occurred to me. Maybe Ryan was one of those. He had a nice house. He had no children to support. He never bought his round in the pub, which was always a sign of wealth.

It would be yet one more reason to show the world how mistaken it was.

I drove there on a Thursday morning. The previous evening Laura and I had had a blazing row over money, after she had snooped into my desk and seen the credit card statement I had accidentally left on the top.

I tried leaving another message on Abbie's phone, but she'd changed numbers.

When I got up there were two demanding letters from my other credit card companies.

I could take no more. I don't think anybody could have taken any more.

I printed out How To Write a Suicide Note, because I thought it would be quite typical of Laura to ignore or not see a post-it note, even if it was nailed to my monitor.

The book wasn't perfect, some of it was in the wrong order, and the chapter on Calligraphy wasn't finished, and I hadn't written a proper conclusion, and I'd left out loads of Fact Boxes, but you can fiddle around too much sometimes.

I put it on my desk, with a little scribbled note telling Laura that here was enough money to solve all our problems, and that I forgave her, and I drove to Ryan's house.

I wasn't entirely sure, at that moment, what I would do. I had no dynamite, and no gunpowder.

So I would do what any great artist does.

I would improvise.

Use this page as a check list to see if you've understood and used all the useful points I've made so far*

	Understood	Used
Point 1		
Point 2		
Point 3		
Point 4		
Point 5		
Point 6		
Point 7		
Point 8		
Point 9		
Point 10		
Point 11		
Point 12		
Point 13		
Point 14		
Point 15		

*   *Another way to fill up a page!*

chapter twenty-three

Translations

I hope I haven't given the impression that a How To Write writer's life is full of gloom. Quite the contrary. There are extraordinary moments of fulfilment, and one of the greatest of those happened to me five years ago, on June 30th, when I received a phone call.

At first I assumed I was being cold-called about some dubious timeshare operation, as the accent of the caller was rather incomprehensible (almost as bad as a Scotsman's). After a while I realised even the bungling operators of "*Congratulations! Inc*" wouldn't hire someone with an accent so foreign no one could understand what he was saying.

Eventually, after much requests for repetition on my side, and repetition on his, I discovered that his name was Kestutis Maciulis, and he was calling from Vilnius in Lithuania, and he had read my ***How To Write a Poem for Your Local Newspaper***, liked it very much, and wanted permission to translate the text into Lithuanian, with a view to publication.

Naturally I agreed immediately, and as the book was out of print I could see no obstacle to his continuing.

He spent a long time on that first phone call telling me how much the book had meant to him, or I think that's what he said, his grasp of English being somewhat shaky — though I assumed he had a full grasp of Lithuanian, which was the important thing!

My book, he said, had influenced him and inspired his writing of poetry more than any other work of literature, and was, indeed, the reason he had himself become a writer. Well, I think his actual words were, "I write because you book," but I understood what he meant.

He sent a contract very promptly, which I signed and returned, even though it was written in Lithuanian. I trusted him, and that's very important in our work.

I heard nothing for a year or so, though I never gave up hope that I'd see the result, because I realised it wasn't a five minute job, converting and capturing my style and fluency into a strange language.

Sure enough, in the August following the phone call, I received, as an e-mail attachment, a copy of:

Tu Esi Mano Maza Seksualus Kaciukas by **Brin Piodik**, translated by Kestutis Maciulis. *Brangusis Press*. 250 pages. 2000.

I must confess I printed out all 250 pages, even though I didn't understand a word, because there is such a deep satisfaction in knowing that your words have left the parochial home and spread their wings and flown into the world.

It's as if the Tower of Babel never existed. I now spoke to the entire planet. Language no longer divided us, it connected us together.

It was a moment in my How To Write career I shall always treasure. It's true, I never did see a published copy of the book, nor heard from Kestutis Maciulis again, though I still have hopes I will. Perhaps he had his problems, as we all do. He struggled against the Lithuanian Literary Mafioso as I have struggled against the British one, and perhaps he failed.

But no one can deny the work he put in, those long hours studying my sentences and toiling to imitate their cadences. I still keep my copy of *Tu Esi Mano Maza Seksualus Kaciukas* in my room, as one of my treasured possessions, and open a page sometimes, at random, and read out a few words.

Kestutis Maciulis, I thank you.

And if other How To Write writers can be as fortunate as I was, they will consider themselves lucky, as I do.

You can, of course, translate your work, or have it translated, not just into other languages, but other media, although this may prove to be just as difficult as getting it published in book form. I still have the screenplay of **How To Write a Novel About Modern Working-Class Life**, a project to which I devoted almost a year.

At first I saw it as the story of a working-class lad who got a job as a binman instead of going to university because he didn't want to sell out, and then wrote a wonderful novel about his life because he had happened across a book which showed him how to do it, called, of course, **How To Write a Novel About Modern Working-Class Life**.

It had everything. Grit, the north, girls, pubs, even the kitchen sink.

The Fiction Factory didn't want to know. Nor Hammer Films, Hat Trick Productions, Picture Palace Films, Working Title, Zenith, Scala Productions, Parallax, or any of the other 300 independent film companies of this country.

I made it Scottish and put lots of drug references in and sent it to Ewan McGregor and then Robert Carlyle. I never heard a word.

I put it to one side, and one day had the remarkable idea of turning it into a kind of documentary. I have quite a good broadcasting manner (I was once interviewed in the street about the ring road, and saw it later on Midlands Today and I came over rather well) and felt I could do a good job of introducing it, although if they wanted Melvyn Bragg I wouldn't stand in his way.

I saw it with lots of location filming, in gritty northern industrial towns, dark men-only type pubs, and one episode spent following a group of binmen around the town.

I spent a lot of time and energy adapting my screenplay, and I think it still stands as one of the classics of TV.

But the BBC weren't interested, nor ITV, Channel 4, Sky, or anyone else. Not even the Discovery Channel, UK History, or BBC 3 or 4, for godsake, and the rubbish they put out.

I didn't give up. I'm not a quitter. I thought, there are other media. DVDs, I thought, they'd be perfect.

I wrote to the company that made *Half Life*, and then the

one that made *Civ IV*, suggesting an educational DVD for aspiring writers, a series, starting with **How To Write a Novel About Modern Working-Class Life**.

They were very nice, polite, wrote that they only did games, but how about contacting an educational DVD publisher? They didn't enclose a free copy of any of their games, unfortunately, but otherwise I was most impressed.

So I found an educational DVD publisher off the net, and entered into a very fruitful dialogue with them. They quite liked the idea, but wanted me to expand on how I saw it working. Well I hadn't a clue, that's not my speciality, I'm a writer and not a computer programmer, and I told them so, because that's the best way to approach companies. Be direct, and straight. Don't try and mess about and pretend you know more than you do.

I didn't hear from them again, for some reason, probably my letter got lost, but the idea had got me fired up and I spent a long time on the computer, wondering how you could adapt *Civ IV* or *SimCity* for a series of How To Write DVDs. I certainly became an expert on *Civ IV*, and *SimCity*. I took over the world on several occasions, and built some wonderful cities.

But it wasn't until I wrote **How To Write a Stinking Letter of Complaint** that I saw the light. This was the perfect opportunity to make full use of the medium. Just click, and fill in the blanks, print it out, and there you have your perfect letter:

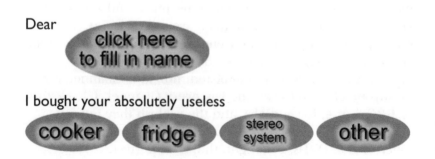

in

> click here to fill in date A

It stopped working on

> click here to fill in date B

I've had it with electrical goods failing after

> date A - date B = C

weeks.

I want a full refund of

> click here to fill in amount A

plus an extra

> click here to fill in amount B

for my inconvenience, making

> amount A - amount B = amount C

You're an absolute disgrace, and should be bloody well ashamed of yourselves.

Looking forward to your reply, and it had better be soon, or else,

Yours faithfully

> click here to fill in name

You see how easy it would be? I had about 500 letters like that one, all graded from polite (like that one) to obscenely abusive. I used to look at some of them when I got cross with something that didn't work and it always made me feel better.

It was a winner.

But could I get anyone to be interested in it? Could I hell.

The blindness in this country that won't reward innovation. We invent the railways, the jet engine, hovercraft, TV, penicillin, and everything else that's any use. And do we applaud our creative people? Never.

I would have done it myself, put it all on DVD, well I did, I copied the manuscript with a DVD copier, but I couldn't do all the fancy stuff, the video parts, the clicking, the whole look of it.

I'm still convinced it can be done. I just need someone who can put my ideas into practice. The idea that if you build a better mousetrap the world will beat a path to your door is so much dreamy nonsense. I know. I've built so many better mousetraps I could rid the world of vermin. Instead, we're always within five metres of a rat, wherever we are. And in the publishers' and agents' part of London, a lot closer.

I ought to mention, on a more upbeat note, my **How To Write 1991 Calendar** for my first publishers, Crocker & Thistle. Each month contained the covers and excerpts from, sadly, mainly other writers' How To Write Books. Though if you turn to October, there is the rather art deco cover of **How To Write a Novel About Modern Working-Class Life**, and at the bottom of the page a quote from the book, advice that is still pertinent today:

"The writer must live his work. The reader will know if you're pretending. There's no substitute for reality!"

I still keep that calendar, because in 2015 it'll have the right days again, and, if you ignore the "Dentist 3.15" and "Pay milk today" scribbles, will once more be useful.

And never more useful than when it's October.

chapter twenty-four

Bursaries and grants

I get shouted down in the pub for saying this, but I've never been afraid of being controversial if it's the truth:

Mrs Thatcher was right about a lot of things.

She always said that artists shouldn't get money off the government. If they can't sell whatever they're producing, they should find another job.

Which is exactly correct, and personally I've never expected handouts.

Every one of my books has or would have sold well. If they didn't it wasn't Mrs Thatcher's fault. If she had had a free rein, and not been held back by the British establishment, she would have privatised the dustbin service, and though I don't bear grudges — if someone hurts me I may get angry for a few minutes, but then it's forgotten, life's too short — but I would have seen all my old colleagues out on the street and begging to have their jobs back at a quarter of their old wages, and now see who's laughing last.

FACT BOX 45

And in case you've been talking down the Golden Lion to Mad Mac, who is always arguing with me about this, the money I receive from the DHSS at the moment is purely temporary, and forced by circumstances. It's also less than the amount of money Paul McCartney earns in 0.00000000000000000000000000000000000-000000001 of a second, which is the smallest unit of time there is (the unit known as the Planck time), so don't try and make me feel guilty.

I don't know why I ever put in a chapter called "**Bursaries and Grants**", though I always do, even in my *How To Write a Poem for Your Local Newspaper*, and I can scarcely imagine anyone getting a grant to write a piece of doggerel, though they couldn't have a smaller chance than me, the number of applications to various branches of the Arts Council I've sweated over.

Arts Council says it all really. Arts, that aspiring and inspiring word, next to Council, possibly the dullest concept ever invented. I once attended a council meeting — our local town council, not the Arts Council — and it was the dullest two hours I've ever endured. I wasn't doing research, no book is worth writing that needs that kind of research, it was to do with a planning application, as our next-door neighbour wanted to build a double garage and extension (another personal attack on our liberty by Mr Stacey).

Unfortunately, I was asleep when that item came up, and Laura was at her yoga class, so it got approved.

I don't know what else they spent the evening talking about. Whether to put a hump or a bump or a chicane or red markings outside a primary school. Whether to have a noticeboard three foot or three foot six inches above the ground.

And these are the people in charge of deciding which artists get grants and which don't!

Well, not them exactly, but people very like them.

I never got a penny, even though I applied for some rather wonderful projects. And not arty farty useless projects, but really practical ideas for the general community. Like going round graveyards for my projected **How To Write a Gravestone Inscription**.

Rejected, despite the often completely inadequate and unimaginative bald statements you see in burial grounds, as if the idea that you're only able to state: "Joe Bloggs 1930-2004," is somehow set in stone.

Or my **How To Write a Letter Blocking a Planning Application**, where I asked for only a few thousand quid to attend town council meetings. It's all right, I wasn't really going

Piddock researching 'How To Write a Gravestone Inscription' *

to attend, I'd rather have died, I was just going to chat instead to Dave, Jack the Hack's mate, whose job is to report on council meetings.

A brilliant and eminently necessary book, filling a wide hole in the market.

Rejected.

---

* *Right. That's it. I mean this is sick. I'm sorry, I've got as good a sense of humour as anyone else alive, but I do not find that funny. No, I'm going to ring the publishers and tell them, I want Connolly's drawings out of this book. All of them. It's my book, and I'm not putting up with nasty and abusive scribbles like this. Either his drawings go, or I'm not letting them publish the book, and that's final. I mean it. He's gone too far this time.*

Of course there's no money left, after all those bureaucrats on the Arts Council have taken their fat fees and bloated expenses. The Arts Council budget for this year is £161.5 million, and after paying their salaries and expenses, there's £12,000 left, which last year went to a mate of the chairman who wanted to build a shed in his garden. I'm speaking metaphorically here, of course (see *Fact Box 28*). And of course, they had to make some cuts and they managed to save some money by never using the word "Accepted" in their letters, which meant there was now enough for a crate of vintage claret for the executive committee.

I don't want to think about them. They're worse than publishers, and publishers are the bacteria that float on scum.

I'd rather think of better, pleasanter, positive things.

FACT BOX 46

O*f course I ought to stress that I exclude the publishers of this book, even if they have picked a crock in Connolly, from all those publishers and agents and other middlemen and women who do nothing except take the nits out of each other's hair and couldn't pick a bestseller from a pile of unsolicited manuscripts if it was printed on £20 notes.*

And except for D L Guppy, now I think about it. They published How To Write a Poem for Your Local Newspaper, and I'm sure would have published more of my works, if they hadn't had a disastrous year in 1999 and had to cease trading.

Except Crocker & Thistle, too, now I think about it. After all, they published How to Write a Working-Class Novel and the How to Write 1991 Calendar with its October spread. I owe them a lot. They started me on this path. Without them, I'd still be a maths teacher, a family man with a wife and two children and a house and garden. I can't express enough gratitude to them. I think I shall write

> *to them, and say so, not in any spirit of wanting anything,*
> *but just to spread a little happiness. And mention at the*
> *same time, in a postscript, that I do happen to have a*
> *recent work they might be interested in.*

I can't think of any better, pleasanter, positive things.

I'll tell you instead about that Thursday morning, when I took that drive to Ryan's house. It was probably the worst day of my life, but I'd still rather think of that than the Arts Council.

I knew Ryan wouldn't be at home, because he teaches at the local college on Mondays and Thursdays. Drama. I will acknowledge that he's probably very good at drama, how else can someone be so skilfully deceptive, all pleasantries to me while he's sleeping with my wife?

I admit I was very angry. It had built up, and I don't think I would have been human if the pressure hadn't had to be released in some way. But I took no weapons or implements of any sort. I could have done. I had a gallon of petrol in the garage. I admit I'd forgotten I had a gallon of petrol in the garage, but if I had been so inclined I could have gone in there and looked. I didn't even bring a jemmy or ladder for breaking in, or a box of matches or a lighter. I had nothing planned. I would do what I had to do, and once there I would know what I had to do.

Whatever, it was going to be, and I knew this and was certain about it, spectacular. No, not 'speccy', thank you, bloody Australians.

Spectacular.

I parked the car and put the balaclava over my face, and walked along the disused railway line. I'd crossed the field by the hedge and kept very low as I went along the fences at the bottom of the gardens, so that no one would see me, until I reached the fence at the back of Ryan's house. I nipped over the fence quite easily and ran from tree to tree across the lawn.

I went to his back door, and there was my first surprise.

The door was open, and the glass in one of the frames was smashed.

The back door leads into a corridor that goes straight through the house to the front door. I looked cautiously in, and as I couldn't hear anyone, I walked through the door and into the hall. The living room door was half closed, but I could hear some noise there, a thud, so I pushed open the door, ready, if it was Ryan, with a cheery quip.

FACT BOX 47

I saw Kurt in town yesterday afternoon. Strange man. He seemed to see me, and went off in another direction. I wouldn't be surprised if he didn't end up one of these crazy people who stand outside Woolworths and shout to themselves. It's always the straight and apparently stable ones that happens to. Life is full of surprises. Important to remember that. You can invent the most implausible events, and it won't be less plausible than reality.

As the door swung open I saw that everything in the room seemed to have been tipped over, and in the middle of the room was a pile of paper and books. A man stood, his back to me, by the bookshelf, pulling books out as if clearing it ready to be cleaned, though not caring where or how they landed.

"Excuse me," I said. "Where's Ryan?"

The man swung round. The cigarette between his lips dropped to the floor as his mouth opened. He spoke a quiet but rather violent swear word, and strode towards me. I moved quickly aside, but he went past and had opened the front door and left before I could say anything, or even get a good view of his face.

I tried to work out what was going on, who Ryan had employed, possibly a decorator or a handyman, or whether he was moving house and no one had told me. I heard a crackling noise at my feet, and looked down and realised that one of the pieces of paper had caught fire, and was beginning to flame a little, probably lit by the man's discarded cigarette.

Careless, I thought, very dangerous, an unattended fire in the middle of the carpet, and I was about to stamp it out, or at least pick it up and put the burning bits in the fire grate, when I noticed a bound manuscript, open and face upwards at the top of the pile.

I picked it up, and looked at its front. It said:

The Craft of Writing a Craft of Writing Book, by Ryan Jinks.

I almost fell into the armchair, and began to leaf slowly through it. Not too bad, I thought, despite his usual errors, punctuation, lack of Fact Boxes, and tedious personal anecdotes.

I must have looked at it for some while and been quite engrossed, despite the room becoming quite smoky, because a car pulling up outside roused me, and when I looked up the flames had now spread, and there was something of a blaze in the middle of the room.

I dropped the manuscript back on the floor and looked through the window. It was a police car. I thought to myself, "This won't look good, you know. Me, in my balaclava, fingerprints everywhere. I'd better do something, and quickly."

I closed the living room door from the inside, went back to the fire that was now burning well, and noticed that I'd happened to drop Ryan's manuscript in the middle of the blaze. I made an attempt to rescue it, by pulling at its pages, but unfortunately only succeeded in opening it up to the flames.

I gave up and walked across the living room and into the open door of his study.

It was a complete mess in there, everything tipped up, papers that hadn't been dropped in the living room strewn on the floor.

I looked on his desk.

His computer had been taken.

That was terrible for him, but I looked at the pile of copied CDs on the desk and noticed one that said *The Craft of Writing a Craft of Writing Book*, and picked it up to rescue it.

I went back to the living room, coughing and choking, and stumbled through the smoke to the door. Somewhere on that journey I must have dropped the CD, because I didn't have it with me when I reached the hall, desperate for air, as two young policeman barged open the front door.

"Hello," I said to them. "That's a bit of luck. I was just going to ring for you."

chapter twenty-five

Awards and festivals

A wards:
Well, you're allowed to dream, aren't you?

I almost didn't bother to deny it. What was the point? I am dogged by this writer's curse of always being able to see both sides, and from the other side it looked an open and shut case.

But I also possess the writer's curse of always needing to adhere to the truth, and that's what I did.

Actually, I have been to a couple of awards ceremonies. Not long after the publication of **How To Write a Novel About Modern Working-Class Life** I was invited to join the *Association Of British How To Write Writers*, and eagerly accepted the honour.

My publishers were thrilled for me, and I didn't mind paying the fee of £200 a year, well worth it, I believed, to be considered part of that august body.

Soon after, I got an invitation to the 1994 awards ceremony of the *Association of British How To Write Writers*. Well, I didn't know what other How To Write Books had been published in

---

FACT BOX 48

There is another, rival, organisation, The Craft of Writing Writers' Guild of Great Britain, *a much older and more conservative organisation, and I wouldn't recommend them at all. They didn't ask me to join, anyway, so they can sod off.*

1994, and frankly I didn't care, I never read other How To Write Books and I never will, but I was very confident that there wouldn't be a better How To Write Book than mine.

I sent off my £100 for the dinner, and hired a suit, and Laura got a ball gown, and looked very fetching, and we got the train to London.

It was a very nice spread, buffet, all you could eat, and the first drink was free, though we were sat next to some total nonentities, the man on my right probably the most boring person in the world, all he could talk about was himself. Talk about writer's ego. He wasn't interested in anything I had to say.

Then we came to the awards. There were a few for *Best Book Cover*, and *Most Unusual Font, Most Original Title*, and *Best Use of Punctuation*, until we reached the important ones.

"*Best Newcomer.*"

I wasn't even nominated! Some woman won it. I didn't even hear what she had written.

Then I realised, of course, they wouldn't nominate me for *Best Newcomer,* because I'm *Best New or Old Comer, Best Every Comer*. As in the next award:

"*Best How To Write Book of 1994.*"

At that moment the boring man started to say something to me, and because I had to shut him up I missed the nominations. I didn't care. Everyone was looking at me and applauding, I had my speech in my hand, I was on my feet, I was about to walk up to the stage when Laura pulled at my jacket, and the most boring person in the world stood and walked past me to the podium.

I carried on standing — it can be rather embarrassing, that moment, if you've stood and it isn't you that's been announced — and pretended I was doing it to turn the applause into a standing ovation, but the standing ovation didn't happen, so I had to stand on my own for several seconds before sitting eventually anyway, which was just as embarrassing.

I did get a look at the award, and hold it in my hand, when the boring man came back, after his boring speech. It had a

The award for the Best How to Write Book of 1994 *

rather tinny feel to it, certainly not heavy enough to hit him over the head, as I'd have liked.

It was so painful — being next to that pompous twerp as people came up to him and congratulated him, the insincerity oozing off them, the hypocrites — that after I told him how

---

* I rang publisher Neil Rhodes, and I told him I didn't really approve of some of Anthony Connolly's drawings and captions, and he said if I wanted to take the book to another publisher I was quite welcome, but Anthony Connolly was his brother-in-law and he wasn't going to put up with a whole load of grief from his wife and family because of my oversensitive feelings. That's what he said. In fact he said the only reason he was publishing this book was to give his brother-in-law a start in his career and he didn't care what I did, there was always some other writer he could get.
So I'm having a long and careful think about it.

pleased I was for him and thought his book was marvellously well written and he certainly deserved every award going, I went off to the bar to get sloshed.

I don't remember getting home that night. Laura apparently called a cab and I was put in it by some Association members. I certainly have no recollection of the fight that Laura described afterwards, and I wouldn't have believed her if it hadn't been for the large black bruise on my cheek and my aching ribs. I'm sure the other bloke, whoever he was, came off worse.

I was never invited again, jealousy I suspect, and I let my Association membership lapse when they didn't ask me to renew it. I wouldn't join *The Craft of Writing Writers' Guild of Great Britain*, especially when I discovered Ryan Jinks was on their Public Lending Rights Committee.

Festivals

Do you want to be in a town bulging with writers and would-be writers and publishers and agents? You do? Well put this book down right now. I'm not going to have it polluted by your eyes. Haven't you learned anything by now? Unless you were planning to wait till the whole lot of them are there and call in an air strike.

No one believed me. Not the police, nor Laura, nor Ryan, nor the Crown prosecution service, nor the court, nor the judge, nor the jury. I don't think my defending counsel believed me, which is very unfair.

Nobody had seen the burglar, even though I gave as good a description as I could, but everyone had seen me. One neighbour, in particular, seemed to spend all her life looking out of her upstairs back window, and had kept a diary of all the times I had previously gone to the bottom of Ryan's garden, with my binoculars and seat and sandwiches. I'm sure I didn't really go there every day for eight weeks, but what was my word against hers, when no one was on my side?

The manuscript of **How To Write a Suicide Note** didn't help, either, as I had made it rather more specific than I'd intended, about the things I was going to do to make Ryan's life an absolute misery. I explained that was a book, and anything specific merely fictional examples, and names would have been removed before publication, but I could see they weren't convinced.

I think the destruction of Ryan's manuscript was the clincher. It didn't do any good for me to insist that I hadn't put it on the fire, even though I hadn't, at first (I don't think replacing something where you found it is a criminal offence, surely? Anyway, I didn't tell them I'd replaced it, just in case. Not that it made any difference, in that kangaroo court).

The trouble was that was some so-called 'evidence' that I had previously deleted a work of Ryan's from his computer — 'evidence' like someone had seen me go into his study and someone had seen me come out, and later Ryan discovered his entire hard drive had been formatted. I still insist that that is all purely circumstantial. Perry Mason wouldn't have allowed it.

There was also the affair that Ryan and Laura had been conducting for some time, but curiously this wasn't mentioned in court. Of course I didn't bring it up, I didn't want to provide them with a motive, and they hadn't got one yet (the prosecuting counsel said something about me being envious of Ryan's success! Me? Envious of him? I did laugh at that. Out loud, it was so preposterous. No one else laughed, but they were probably too thick to see the joke).

The only thing on my side was Ryan's computer. It was never found, and my defending counsel did, I thought, a very good job of sarcastically wondering how I had managed to get rid of it. Buried it in the garden? Put it up my sleeve? Eaten it?

Just my luck then that the prosecution produced the refuse collection schedule, which showed that a bin lorry had passed 15 minutes before I was discovered, plenty of time for me to chuck it in, they said, and then get back to burn his manuscript.

Those bastard binmen. They've blighted my life for 20

years, and now they get me put away.

I think the three months between the case and the sentencing was the worst time. I had to go for psychiatric assessment. I did consider pretending to be psychotic so I wouldn't have to go to prison, but decided to just be myself. I had had enough of pretending. And then the psychiatrist said I was on the verge of being psychotic! Not enough to get off prison, unfortunately.

Then Laura made me move out. I resisted that, but her solicitor, and then my solicitor, told me I hadn't really much choice. In fact they said she was being very nice in allowing me to see my own children. Allowing!

And after a couple of weeks, when I was on a visit to collect some of my old manuscripts, she told me that Ryan was moving in.

She said it as if it was going to shock me, but I told her I'd known for years about her and Ryan. She made up some pathetic story about how they'd only just happened to bump into each other during the trial, and talk, and gone out, and fallen in love.

I didn't debate it with her. If she chose to blight her relationship with Ryan by lying about it, that was her choice.

I had enough to worry about. I had to prepare for a custodial sentence, the judge had told me, and the thought made me physically sick every morning.

I can't deny it, I was terrified.

I certainly couldn't get down to any work.

In conclusion, take it from me, what matters aren't awards and winning. You'll know if you've done a good job and deserve an accolade. If you've been awarded a prize and know deep down it should have gone to someone else, show some honesty, for a change. Tell the world he is the one who should have got the award. Send him the cheque.

You owe it to yourself.

chapter twenty-six

Writers' courses

Writers' courses are propagating like greenfly in a hot dry summer. I unreservedly recommend them. After all, you want to be a How To Write writer and you're unsure how to set out in your new career, what should you do? Spend £500 for a three-day course run by a sozzled has-been in a rural retreat with a bunch of other newbies? Or buy this book at £7.99 including post & packaging?

You think I'm being ironic. Haven't you learnt that I possess a little more subtlety, that I spurn the easy stuff, that I reach beyond irony? I am, indeed, post-ironic. No, I mean it. Go on the course. You won't learn anything about writing, you'll be thoroughly depressed, either because your fellows write rubbish but they're all jumping with so much enthusiasm it makes you want to vomit and become a monk, or they write better than you do and you hate them for it.

But, if you're at all presentable, you'll find someone to have some rumpy-pumpy with, and at your time of life that is much more important than learning anything about writing.

Then buy this book, and learn all there is to learn about writing a How To Write Book.

I went to one of those courses, years ago. Even then I knew that no one was going to be able to teach me anything. That wasn't why I spent my cash. I had just finished my *How To Write an Erotic Romantic Short Story* and thought the easiest way of getting it published was to go on a course, meet a tutor who could look at it, pronounce it wonderful, and send it to his agent, who would get it published within the month.

And I'd get some rumpy-pumpy.

It doesn't work like that (apart from the rumpy-pumpy).

The tutors on that course were ageing married couple Charles and Frieda McKinley. They had jointly written a couple of moderately successful How To Write Books, though both as I recall were written in the old-style: long chapters unbroken by even a subheading, let alone a hint of a Fact Box or useful diagram.

They didn't lead the course in order to help budding How To Write writers. They took the course for the money, obviously, and *then* to identify the best budding How To Write writer and nip that bud before it blossomed and threatened Charles and Frieda.

They savaged my book. They criticised the title, the style, the content.

Eventually I refused to attend their seminars, and stayed in my room, or the local pub. I didn't even get my rumpy-pumpy, although everyone else seemed to. That wasn't my fault, it was just every girl I suggested we go to their room to discuss my manuscript said they would rather go to Charles and Frieda's seminars! Incredible how sycophantic and submissive they all were. I told them, one at a time, a writer has to be a rebel. "But I've paid my £367 for this course," they'd say.

Of course, now that I have more experience in How To Write Books than probably anyone else alive, I ought to be the one leading these courses, but frankly I don't believe in defrauding honest if naive people of their money. I don't want to behave like Charles and Frieda, gathering acolytes to impress with feeble namedropping stories, like the time I saw Brad Pitt in the Gower Street branch of Waterstone's.

I'm developing a bit of a cold, actually. I can feel the dryness in my throat. People who go out to work, and think you're just a skiver for being a writer, don't understand just how difficult it is to keep that self-discipline when you're feeling unwell.

I'm meant to be taking Adam and Jordan to the cinema on Saturday to see some awful cartoon. I'd better tell Laura I can't. It's for their sakes. I don't want to give them a cold. Though now I think about it, they probably gave it to me when I saw them the week before last, the blighters. It isn't easy, being a

---

FACT BOX 49

I did see Brad Pitt in the Gower Street branch of Waterstone's, a couple of years ago. He was buying some plays. I wouldn't have known who he was, except I heard someone say, "Brad Pitt's upstairs, in the theatre section." I didn't rush up, like some others, I just happened to have finished where I was and needed to look at some natural history books (research for my How to Write A How It Changed the World Book), and there he was. I wouldn't have known him if they hadn't said. He's not as tall as he seems to be in his films, nor as blonde.
Not that I paid any attention to him.

---

weekend father. Especially since Jordan's beginning to get some stick at school on account of his large bust and Laura told him that I had insisted he have that name (thank you, Laura).

Not *his* large bust, you understand, but the large bust of the other, more famous, Jordan. Well, whatever a child is called they get teased at school. That's not my fault.

At least I know that Ryan and Laura will never get married, or at least if they do the children will never take his name. Jordan Jinks? I don't think so.

chapter twenty-seven

Conclusion

I haven't tried to give you an exact recipe in this book. Writing isn't like that. If you want to be a successful How To Write writer you're going to have to put something of yourself into your work. You must, as it were, discover your own How To Write Voice.

But I believe that if you diligently follow my advice, and study each chapter, you can't go far wrong. I've provided you with the tools and equipment. In spirit, I will be holding your hand. Your left hand, so you can continue to write. Unless you're left-handed, in which case I will hold your right hand. There's no compulsion for you to put my name on the first page under '*Acknowledgements*', though it would be nice.

You'll have your ups and your downs, your good times and your bad, exhilaration and despair. This is all part of being a How To Write writer.

But nothing of what you feel, unless you're Jeffrey Archer, will be as bad as what I felt in between my court case and my sentencing.

Why didn't I do what I had intended, I thought, and blow myself up in Ryan's house?

Because I hadn't got any dynamite, I reminded myself. Such is the thin line between intention and fulfilment.

I considered appealing against the verdict, but was told that the appeal probably wouldn't be heard before I'd got out of prison.

"So I'm not likely to be given a long sentence?" I said.

"No more than three years," my solicitor told me.

Three years. When you're at your prime and your peak, like me, that's a lifetime. It's a horrible thought, prison, especially when, as in my case, you're innocent. You feel so powerless against the force of society.

I wondered if I should escape to another country, but it would have to be outside the EU, or they'd bring me back to custody, and I wouldn't want to go to America, or Australia, or Asia, or Africa. Anyway, I didn't have any money, not enough for a coach ticket to Dover. I thought about robbing a bank. What had I got to lose? This was how far society was pushing me! But how do you rob a bank these days? I hadn't a clue, and I found that there weren't any handy *How to Rob a Bank* books on Amazon.

I spent a lot of time in the pub, and I don't think anyone can blame me for that. During the days I used to redraft my will — I fully expected never to come out alive, or, if alive, sane — but all I was leaving were a few unpublished manuscripts. Of course, I knew these were good, and there was a very good chance that like Kafka I would be discovered only after my death.

FACT BOX 50

I did consider doing what Kafka did, and request my friends destroy all my work after my death, but I didn't want to take the risk my friends would carry out my wishes. Kafka must have known something about his friends, that they were allergic to smouldering paper, or something, to make such a request. He wouldn't have meant it. I know writers.

But it was equally possible that my lilies were born to blush unseen, and apart from my two lads — who would obviously honour my name and fight for its rehabilitation — the only time I would be remembered would be a sigh in the pub as Jack or Mac or Dan would mention me, and they'd all go quiet, and raise their glasses, and toast my fond memory. And, I hoped, vow never to write anything ever again, as they were partly to blame for causing me to end up in this mess.

But listen, if I've managed to convey a hundredth of the apprehension I was feeling at the thought of spending the rest of my life in prison (I was given nine months, once the old buffer of a judge had made up his mind), even my skill won't be able to convey a thousandth of what that first night behind bars was like.

It was bloody awful.

The whole ritual, taking off your clothes in public, the humiliation, the coarse prison uniform, the unspeakably rude prison officers.

The prisoners.

They were, let's face it, not from the best echelons of society.

I doubt a single one of them would keep to the 30mph speed limit along the road outside my window. And my cell 'mate' was absolutely nothing like Ronnie Barker, except maybe in size. He certainly didn't speak to me in a humorous and affable manner. He didn't speak to me at all.

That first night was easily the worst of my life. It was the sounds that were so horrible, the grunts and crying out and the knocking on pipes and shouts. No, it was that little view of an orange sky through the barred window, that was the most horrible. No, it was the smell, crap and disinfectant and stale male odour, that was the most horrible.

I knew I wouldn't be able to sleep. How could anyone sleep in those circumstances? If I'd had a cyanide pill, I'd have chewed it quite happily. Especially after that so-called meal I'd had, you'd get more vitamins in a cyanide pill.

Amazingly, the second night was even worse than the first, after a day of being shunted around from one place to another, and one awful moment of violence when some brute shoved me in the back because I was a bit slow in the food queue. I wondered then if I was going to have to attack him with my tray to prove myself, but luckily he said, "Sorry, mate," and I simply had to wait for the next time.

The third, and fourth, nights were worse than the first two, and the fifth was worse than all the other ones put together, and I was sure I wouldn't survive nine months, or less for good behaviour. I should, I told myself, have run when I had the chance, anywhere, homeless on the streets of an Australian city, was better than this.

Piddock's prison cell *

*   It was bad. Not like that, but bad. I mean you can tell Anthony Connolly hasn't been inside a prison. Not for want of trying, probably. He probably deals in drugs, so it's only a matter of time.
I thought about what my publishers said, by the way, and I thought, well, I'll let them publish this edition, the first. Later editions I'll give to someone else, and get a proper artist to do some proper drawings. It's not a compromise, not at all. It's just that you need a leg up the greasy pole to get a foot in the door, that's all.

It wasn't so much as what happened, the assaults and the intimidation. I mean, I didn't see any of that. It was the *fear* of been assaulted and intimidated. You never knew what was going to happen next, or who was going to attack you, even when no one attacked you and nothing happened. If something had happened, at least the waiting for something to happen would have ended.

Then, when I thought I was going to snap and have to do something, like hit my cellmate for the way he looked at me in the morning, I was called in for an interview with the Governor.

He was much younger than I expected, in his 30s, probably, someone who looked more like a computer engineer, a manager, I guessed, one of these people who rise quickly on nothing except ambition and drive.

He asked me a few questions, routine things which he probably already knew about, and how I was getting on, and advice to behave, and so on.

He dismissed me, and I was thinking this was all rather a waste of time, although it broke up my day and probably broke up his too, when I reached the door, and he casually said, "Oh, by the way."

I recognised this tactic from Columbo, the TV detective. He will always be halfway out of the room when he'll stop and casually mention something to his chief suspect. It's so the chief suspect doesn't suspect he's the chief suspect, and is just relaxing, and will have no answer to the devastating point that's about to be made to him. So I was quite prepared for any question.

"I hear you're a bit of a writer," he went on. "Is that right?"

Quite prepared for any question, except that one.

"Bit of a writer? I'm a published author. It's my career. My livelihood. It's the reason I'm in this place, because of a misunderstanding on that very subject," was what I thought, but didn't say.

"Yes, sir," is what I said.

"It's just, I have a novel here." He reached behind him and picked up a manuscript from the table. "It's a sort of thriller, I suppose. Based on my life as a prison officer. People I've shown it to have been rather impressed." He folded his hands over his manuscript. "In fact I was a deputy governor at the prison where Jeffrey Archer was held. I showed it to him, and he told me that it was excellent. He did say he'd get his agents to give me a ring, but I haven't heard anything yet. I just wondered if you'd like to have a look. Make any suggestions you want, I'd be happy to take them on board."

"Yes, sir. I'd be delighted."

He handed it over, and I was taken back to my cell.

I read it in a day, and felt even more depressed. It was dreadful. True, it was gripping, and I couldn't put it down, and towards the end I was biting my fingers as I'd bitten away all my fingernails. But he hadn't studied the genre. He had recognisable characters, I mean real people, and had shown some depth in their characterisation. The villain even had some good in him! There wasn't a happy ending where the girl and hero got off together. There was no detailed description of the weaponry used. I could understand the plot!

It was all quite hopeless, but I knew I had a real problem. How could I tell the Governor all this? He had total control over my life. He could make me sole toilet cleaner if he chose. But the one thing I would never do is refuse to tell the truth. I speak what I believe.

Usually. In this case I recognised that I had no choice, and I praised him fulsomely. I even suggested — my masterstroke — that if I could have some access to the library and a computer, I could put together a letter to publishers which would practically guarantee publication for such a masterpiece. This is where my experience came in useful. I knew that the length of time publishers took to respond to an unsolicited manuscript meant I would be far away from there by the time he got the usual rejection slip.

He agreed most willingly, and I offered at the same time to correct the few punctuation and grammatical mistakes if he would give me the book on a floppy disk.

Now, for the first time since I arrived at that place, I began to find a little enjoyment in life. I corrected his errors, and made one or two little improvements, like taking out the hero's foibles, and changing his looks to handsome and strong featured, and the girl to beautiful and blonde, and making the villain a genuine psychopath, and making sure he died horribly and the hero and girl went off to the Caribbean with a lot of money. Just the minor corrections the work needed.

I printed it out, did the usual letter, packaged it up, and sent it to the first five publishers' names in the *Writers' and Artists' Yearbook*.

Unfortunately, they sent it back very quickly, with the usual insulting stuff, clichéd, lacking in depth, old-fashioned, trite characterisation.

I told the Governor we'd try a different approach. I'd write a synopsis of the book and send that, because publishers never read books these days.

I did a beautiful treatment. It may not have stuck too closely to the Governor's book, but was a great improvement on it.

That too came back rather swiftly. I was beginning to wish I hadn't told the Governor his book was so wonderful. Instead I tried to explain about the bitchiness of the publishing industry, and how difficult it was for an outsider to gain admittance.

I could see, however, that he was in danger of losing faith in me, and I decided to take another tack.

"The important thing in publishing," I told him, "is never to be content with just one book. Publishers won't invest in someone who writes one novel, and then goes back to their day job. You should begin your second book immediately, then we can tell the publishers that you're a career novelist. They like that. They'll spend money on you then."

This appealed to him, but, as I suspected, he didn't have a second book. He had put everything he knew into his first one. That was where I came in. I would be his teacher. I would give the course I should have been giving these last 20 years, if only the organisers at Lumb Bank had had the sense to ask me.

He loved the idea. There was so much he wanted to learn about the writing business. He had a vague idea about a book about the girl he'd fallen in love with at University, but he didn't know where to start. I could see he was going to be a dream student.

There was a snag. He couldn't really arrange for the two of us to spend several hours in the week together. It might look wrong. But there was a way round that. I could give a course for every prison officer, and he would come along to it.

It would be useful for them, and time filling and rehabilitative for me.

I wasn't sure, to be honest. I wasn't in prison for nine months in order to work four hours a day. I was meant to be serving my debt to society.

However, you don't disagree with the Governor.

chapter twenty-eight

FAQs

What does FAQ stand for?

Frequently Asked Questions. Everyone knows that. That's not a FAQ, that's a RAQ (Rarely Asked Question).

How do you pronounce FAQ?
Fack, I always say. Or rather think. No one says it. Imagine being in the pub and saying, "I've got a FAQ." It wouldn't happen.

The only time anyone would say the word would be if someone asked, "How do you pronounce FAQ?" Then you'd have a good hour's argument. That's what it's like in the pub. Everyone has an opinion and no one's right except themselves.

I said to Jack the Hack the other day, "Why didn't you tell me about Laura and Ryan? I had a right to know. There's nothing worse than being sniggered about behind your back."

He said he didn't know about it. He said they were all amazed when it came out.

And he calls himself a friend. Well, I don't suppose he does. Drinking companion, I expect he'd say, or just bloke I know from down the pub.

He ought to be called Jack the FAQ. Or Jack Take a Flying FAQ.

I've written a book about carpets, called "The Carpet: How It Changed the World", but incredibly no one would publish it. I followed that up with a book about amoeba, called "The Amoeba: How It Changed the World", but no one will publish that either. I see in this book that you've already established copyright on the title **How to**

Write A How It Changed the World Book. *Can I call my new book*, "Writing A How It Changed the World Book", *or* "A Practical Guide to Writing a How It Changed the World Book"? No! Just put the book aside and start on something else. At least you had the decency not to suggest it was called, "*The Craft of Writing a How It Changed the World Book*", or I'd have you banned from the world of How To Write Books.

How long should my How To Write Book be?
About 60357 words is right. You'll see it has a natural length. Don't try and spin it out with the aid of faddy devices. They won't fool anyone, except maybe a publisher.

How did the writing courses you gave in prison turn out?
Ah. Interesting question. I must admit both the Governor and I were confident that though every prison officer was invited to attend there'd be only him and me in the room. Well, that first evening there were 43 prison officers there.

I said to the Governor, "I thought it was just going to be a little chat. I can't give a lecture to this many people."

He told me to do the best I could, and then he'd divide everyone up into two or three classes, if they were still interested.

It was terrifying, giving a lecture without preparation or notes, but I thought I was doing rather well, outlining the basics of being a writer, when the Governor interrupted me and told me that my explanation of why I was in prison was not appropriate at this moment.

Well, I thought it was appropriate, as a warning, so that they could all see what being a writer might lead to, apart from showing them that I was here because of a miscarriage of justice and should be treated with some respect. But prison is like a totalitarian state, and you don't disobey the Führer.

It seemed to me to be going quite well, when I had the inspiration of going round the room asking these people what writing ambitions they had. I knew some of them quite well by now, and thought I'd be lucky to get more than a "My writing ambition is to spell my name correctly," but I thought it would use up a few minutes of the hour.

The first one, a particularly boneheaded man called Stevens, stood up (this was a subtle ploy of mine, to give them a little taste of the humiliation they gave us every day).

"I've read a few John Grisham books," he said. I was surprised he could read, frankly. "And I think I could do better." Don't we all, darling, I thought. He bent down, and I assumed he was going to sit, because he'd said it all, really. But he stood up, and I saw he had a large pile of paper in his hand. "This is the first draft of my second novel. I think it works quite well. I wondered if you'd have a look at it," he said to me.

"Of course," I said, though it looked to be about a thousand pages long. "I could always sell it as toilet paper. Toilet paper is a valuable currency here, you know."

Actually, I didn't say that last bit. Me, and 43 prison officers and the Governor? No. I just nodded, and he sat, and the next one stood, because I knew Bonehead Stevens would be a fluke.

He wasn't. They had all written novels, or very long short stories, or screenplays that they felt were just right for Hollywood, especially if they could get Vin Diesel or Jean-Claude Van Damme to play the hero, which was of course based on themselves.

It was an absolute nightmare, and at the end of the hour I had several metre-high piles of manuscripts on the table. I told the Governor that I couldn't possibly read all that.

I could tell that he was thoroughly annoyed by his staff, because he wanted my full attention, but in the interests of fairness there wasn't much he could do.

I started the next day, in the library. It was worse than being a Booker Prize judge. At first I was quite scrupulous, reading the whole of Stevens' novel, though I did guess who was the mastermind by page 894. Then little by little I slipped a bit in subsequent manuscripts, and skim read, and then looked at the first chapter and the middle and the end, and finally read the title, the first page, and the last.

A week I spent, in the library. It was like a prison, in there. I used to scream to be let back into my cell.

The trouble was, I didn't know what to do. If I met a prison officer on the landing, he'd say, "What do you think of my book?" And I'd reply, "It was very interesting," or "Well done," or if it was really awful, "You must be very pleased," but he'd want to know, "Is it better then Stevens', or Fatso's?" And I had to quickly work out who was senior, and always make sure I gave more praise to the senior, though sometimes that wouldn't do because a junior could actually be higher in the pecking order than a senior, and I'd get to clean out the toilets.

Seminars were worse. Everyone wanted to talk about their experience of writing, what it meant to them, how they got their ideas, what had happened to them, what computer and word processing programs they had. I wanted to shout, "We don't want to know!" But I had to listen, politely, nodding sagely, hardly ever being allowed to tell them about my experience of writing, which was obviously so much more interesting and valid than theirs.

Then the nightmare suddenly got a lot worse.

My cellmate, who had hardly said a word to me in three months, just an ape-like grunt if he wanted the place to himself, suddenly, one evening after lock-up, spoke a sentence.

"These courses you're giving, to the screws," he said.

"I don't enjoy them," I said quickly. "I don't get any privileges. They make me do it." I was afraid he might think I was a grass or a nark. "It's not through choice."

"I've written a book," he said. "It's a crime book. It's good."

I sat on my bed. I felt nauseous.

"I haven't got it with me, of course. They wouldn't let me bring it in. Anyway, it needs some reworking. The plot isn't quite there. You could help me with it. Help me work out the plot."

I lay down.

"Of course," I said. "Tomorrow. I'll help you tomorrow."

I tried to sleep, but all I could think was, I've got to get out of here. I've got to get out.

FACT BOX 51

The word 'grass', by the way, is cockney rhyming slang from 'grasshopper' = 'shopper'. That was one of the only facts I learnt in prison. The other was that 'nark' derives from 'bark', as in 'dog's bark', 'selling a dog', 'selling' = 'telling'.

What books would you recommend for further reading?
I don't think you could do worse than **How To Write A Poem for Your Local Newspaper**, or **How To Write a Novel About Modern Working-Class Life**. They're both out of print, at the present time, but if you contacted publishers Crocker & Thistle and whoever took over the assets of DL Guppy and really badgered them, perhaps they'd bring out new editions. It's about time.

Is the traffic still bad outside your room?
Worse, every day. Prison was quieter.

Yes, go on about your time in prison.
Oh, all right. Except there's not much more to tell.

It turned out that there were another 64 prisoners who had written, or were in the process of writing, or wanted to write, novels or screenplays, mostly crime or thrillers, though George the Axe-Slasher McQueen had written a Chick-lit novel.

I told the Governor he had to do something about this situation, get me an assistant, or obtain an early release, or employ me full-time, but he wasn't sympathetic.

"I'm afraid it's not my concern anymore, because I'm leaving," he said.

"What, leaving to go to another prison?"

"No, leaving the prison service. I've decided to become a full-time writer. I sent off my original manuscript and it's been accepted by Random House. It comes out in December."

I spent another miserable two months trying to steer an impossible course between discouraging people so they wouldn't send off their manuscripts and get them published, and being nice so I wouldn't get beaten up or my sentence increased.

Luckily I was saved by the new Governor, who was an old-fashioned stickler who didn't believe in extraneous projects and abolished my courses. I liked that man. He was what a prison governor should be, even though all the prisoners and prison officers hated him.

I was released after serving the longest six months of my life. I could hardly carry all the boxes of manuscripts I had to take out, because I'd have got a knife in the back or an extra three months if I'd refused everyone's plea to "try and get it published".

I got the taxi driver to pause by a skip, once we were out of sight of the prison, and I dumped the lot.

That was a reckless thing to do, as it turned out, because I soon got letters and phone calls when I'd moved into my first room, asking how I was getting on with their book.

This is the third room I've got, and I didn't leave a forwarding address, but those people have contacts, and sometimes I fear for my life, even though the prison is 100 miles away.

In fact I dream about it. I wake in the middle of the night and imagine all those manuscripts pouring down on me and I can't breathe because all those words and that paper are suffocating me.

One day, I know, I'll look out of the window and they'll all be there, outside this house, the biggest criminal gang in history, all demanding to know, "When's my book going to be published!"

Have you forgiven Ryan, and Laura, yet?
Oh yes. But I'm a forgiving sort of chap. It's true, they put me through hell, robbed me of a significant portion of my life, and they haven't said a word of apology. I suspect they may not even think there's anything to apologise for!

Of course, I feel slightly sorry for Ryan, and not just because he has to put up with Laura. Apparently he was so

The tell-tale manuscripts *

disheartened (so Sam Sum told me) about the second loss of a
work, in that fire that I didn't start and computer I didn't steal
(and really, Ryan, you should have learned by now — back up!)
that he gave up on that book, whatever it was.

Stick to teaching drama, Ryan, I say.

As for Laura, I doubt she's happy, not since her company
took over that multinational and she's the President and has to
spend so much time in New York and Rome and Tokyo.

---

*   *Thanks, Connolly. I really needed reminding of that.*

And what about you, Brian? What are your plans?
Thanks for asking, but I'm merely the author of this book, not its subject.

Though sometimes I just think, why do I stay in this country? I could leave it all, nothing holding me here, and go anywhere.

Australia, even. The climate's great there. And I'm sure every Australian isn't as bad as the ones I've met so far. Melbourne, I hear, is rather pleasant.

What's the best way to end a How To Write Book?
There are no hard and fast rules on this. But whatever you do, don't drag it out and out-stay your welcome. Less Is More, remember!

You'll know, when you've reached the end.

chapter twenty-nine

Epilogue

I love writing.
I believe I said that in the beginning (I'm not going to check. I don't believe in looking back. Move forward, that's my motto).

But perhaps what I should have said is:

"I love writing about writing."

Or, to be strictly true:

"I love thinking about writing about writing."

Or even:

"I love writing about thinking about writing about writing."

Or — this is it:

"I love thinking about writing about thinking about writing about writing."

And the reason I love thinking about writing about thinking about writing about writing? Because I have a gift. That gift isn't granted to everyone. It's given to very few. If you don't have that gift then, frankly, despite all my best efforts in this book, it'd be better you didn't even start. Leave that page blank. It'll look better that way.

I'm grateful I have a gift. It's the reason I'll probably stay in this country, because, ungrateful and unappreciative though this country may be, it's my country!

FACT BOX 52

Plus Jack the Hack from down the pub tells me that now
I have a criminal record I won't be able to emigrate to
Australia. Australia! Home of the convict! I should have mur-
dered someone. Murdered someone and then murdered the
English language, then they'd have let me in. The bastards.

Piddock celebrating *

---

*   *That's Mr Piddock to you, Connolly.*
And what's that in my hand? Is that an Australian flag? How dare you. How dare you!
Mind you, he can insult me all he wants now, because I got a letter from my old cellmate,
asking me for my opinion on his novel, and I said I hadn't got it any more. I'd handed it
over to someone better qualified than me. Someone called Anthony Connolly. And then I
gave my old cellmate Connolly's address.
Sleep easy, Connolly.

Appendixes
[Or is it appendices? I must check in the library this afternoon]

Appendix 1
Appendices [*I think*]

You have to have at least one appendix to give a professional look to your book. Any scraps of notes you discover you haven't put into the main book, shove them in here.

I had an argument with DL Guppy over this, for my **How To Write a Poem for Your Local Newspaper**. They said that including a list of every local newspaper in the country was unnecessary (despite it taking up 12 pages, and when you're paid by the page that's not insubstantial).

I sent them a letter stating, quite clearly, "Do not remove my appendix!" But they did, anyway, without any consent from me. Their heavy handed approach left a scar which, I feel, still hasn't properly healed, and whenever I think about what they did I get a throbbing pain in my gut.

Appendix 2
Proof reading

Do get someone to look through your book. Someone professional, who can iron out those spelling mistakes and get rid of any of those square brackets the printer's been too negligent to take out!

And don't use a journalist, like Jack the Hack. Journalists can't spell, for starters. Actually, I checked this myself, and I'm rather plessed about it. If you want a job done well, do it yourslef!

Appendix 3
Bibliography

The Dark Interloper, by **Brian Piddock**. 42 pages. 1979 (unpublished, at the present time)

The Walking Wounded by **Brian Piddock**. 562 pages. 1982 (unpublished, at the present time)

Refuse, by **Brian Piddock**. 337 pages. 1985 (unpublished, at the present time)

How To Write a Novel About Modern Working-Class Life by **Brian Piddock**. 152 pages. *Crocker & Thistle*, 1994 (out of print, at the present time)

How To Write An Erotic Romantic Short Story by **Brian Piddock**. 113 pages. *The Modesty Press*, 1996 (out of print, at the present time)

How To Write a Poem for Your Local Newspaper by **Brian Piddock**. 134 pages. *DL Guppy*, 1999 (out of print, at the present time)

How To Write a Stinking Letter of Complaint by **Brian Piddock**. 164 pages. 2002 (unpublished, at the present time)

Tu Esi Mano Maza Seksualus Kaciukas by **Brin Piodik** translated by Kestutis Maciulis. 250 pages. *Brangusis Press*, 2000 (still in print!) (possibly)

How To Write a Suicide Note by **Brian Piddock**. 316 pages. 2004 (unpublished, at the present time)

How to Write A How It Changed the World Book by **Brian Piddock** (almost started)

Appendix 4
Example letter to publishers

Here's an example of the kind of letter you should send to a publisher. It was the one I used for this book, and has been honed after many years of thought:

Dear [*next publisher on list*]

I know you receive many manuscripts every week, and most you don't even bother to look at, you just pretend you've read them. Well you can stop pretending now, because the manuscript inside this envelope is going to change your life. Call a meeting. Ring the directors. Tell your wife/husband you'll be home late. Because you've been chosen to receive:

How To Write a How To Write Book

by me, **Brian Piddock**.

Whoever publishes it is going to make their fortune, believe me, so stop pinching yourself and asking why you're the lucky one I've chosen, just ring my phone number **NOW**.

You [*next publisher on list*] are the first publisher I've sent this to, but I have to tell you that if I haven't heard from you within **24 HOURS** I will assume you're too stupid to recognise a good thing when you see it, and will immediately contact [*next publisher on list*] instead, and you'll be the laughing stock of the publishing world when it's the biggest seller of the year.

Yours faithfully

Brian Piddock

I think you'll agree that this letter stands out from the usual, "I enclose for your consideration" drivel. This will catch the eye of the person who opens the envelopes, and if it doesn't he or she shouldn't be working there.

Appendix 5
Useful names and addresses

I never did manage to track down that list of How To Write publishers. Well I'm sure you can go to a bookshop or the library and look in a How To Write Book as easily as I can. Honestly.

Appendix 6
The Lithuanian language

Frank the Ape has told me that his son-in-law comes from Lithuania, and that his son-in-law says that *Tu Esi Mano Maza Seksualus Kaciukas* doesn't mean "How To Write a Poem for Your Local Newspaper", it means "You are my little sex kitten".

This is yet another example of Frank's rather pathetic sense of humour.

Index

Abbie 163-168

Ape, Frank the 135, 222

Application, How To Write a Letter Blocking a Planning 184

Australia 130, 149, 218

Babbler, a rusty throated wren 146, 148

Bible, King James 122

Block, External Factor Writer's 106-107

Block, First Page Writer's 105-106, 109

Block, First Word Writer's 106

Block, Mid-Work (Complacency Syndrome) Writer's 106, 109

Block, Mid-Work Writer's 106

Block, Writer's 111

Book, How To Write 7-8, 10, 12-14, 26, 28-30, 32, 45-46, 57-58, 60, 62, 64, 66, 68-70, 72-74, 76, 78, 80-82, 84, 86-88, 90, 92-94, 104, 106, 108, 110, 112, 114-116, 118, 120-122, 124-126, 128, 130, 143-144, 146, 148, 192-194, 196, 210, 212, 214, 216, 220-222

Book, How to Write A How It Changed the World 199, 220

Books, How To Write 1, 5-7, 16, 50, 54, 71, 84, 92, 191-192

Box, Fact 122-124, 127, 130

Boxes, Fact 122-125, 129-130

Calendar, How To Write 1991 182

Civilisation IV 50

Comedy, Dante's Divine 124

Complaint, How To Write a Stinking Letter of 123, 133, 141, 149, 152, 180, 220

Connolly 140, 162, 173, 186, 193, 204, 215, 218

Connolly, Anthony 70

Desire, Sick With 22

Diane 18-23, 46-47, 51-53, 58, 75-76, 97-101, 140
Dirt, Giving the 11
Dumped 11
Earth, bloodsucking scum of the 139
Edinburgh 76-79, 97-98, 100-102, 130
'h' 28-29
Hack, Jack the 135-136, 150, 185, 209, 218
Half Life 179
Half Life 2 55
Hamlet 123
Hedgehog, Fruggles the Friendly ixx
Holly 160-166
How To Write Books 174
Inscription, How To Write a Gravestone 184
Interloper, The Dark 1-3, 11, 220
Jinks, Ryan 209
Joyce, James 58-59, 61-62
Junk, Leftover 11
Kaciukas, Tu Esi Mano Maza Seksualus 178
Kafka 111, 202
Kurt 18-20, 46, 51-53, 57, 74, 76-78, 97-101, 139, 149, 188
Landfill, Lords of 11
Life, How To Write A Novel About Modern Working-Class 16-
    17, 33, 35-37, 39-40, 54, 59, 171, 179-180, 182, 191, 213,
    220
Lion, Golden 50, 183
Literature, How To Write a Novel That Will Be Studied at A-
    level English 60, 65
Lorraine 19-20, 46-47, 58, 75-76
Love, The Tonsils Of 22
Mac, Mad 135
Maciulis, Kestutis 177-178, 220
Market, Know your 41
McEwan, Ian 95
Measure, Measure for 66
Newspaper, How To Write a Poem for Your Local 66-67, 177,
    184, 186, 213, 219-220, 222

Noseful, Get a 11

Note, How To Write a Suicide 153-155, 157, 166-169, 172, 175, 195, 220

Novel, How To Write a High Concept Science-Fiction 90-91, 93, 123

Novel, How to Write a Working-Class 186

Odyssey, 2001: A Space 93

Pete, Rowdy 135

Piddock, Brian 2, 3, 10, 16, 17, 22, 40, 66, 113, 141, 143, 156, 173, 185, 204, 218, 220, 221

Piodik, Brin 178, 220

Plot, How To Write A Really Good Crime 19-20

Publishers — see "bloodsucking scum of the earth"

Radio 4 66

Refuse 220

Rhodes, Neil 193

Rooney, Wayne 81-82, 85, 132

Roses, Smelling like 13, 16-17

Shakespeare, William 66, 89, 143

Simms, Miss vii, ix

Space, Waste of 11

Story, How To Write An Erotic Romantic Short 22, 33, 37-39, 43, 54, 59, 65, 84, 149, 155, 158-159, 197, 220

Sue 34

Sum, Sam 135

Swift, Graham 95

Tu Esi Mano Maza Seksualus Kaciukas 220, 222

Ulysses 58, 62

Van, Dan the 56, 135

Wake, Finnegans 58, 60-61, 63

Walk, The Wounded 4

Wes 33-35

Wounded, The Walking 3, 11, 220

Writer, Finest How To Write 157

Writer, How To Write 1, 3, 5-6, 28-29, 45, 47, 57, 111, 197-198

Writer?, So You Want to Be a 85

Order extra copies of
"**How to write a how to write book**"
by Brian Piddock

The perfect present!
Give to all your friends and family!

Cut out and send to:
Brian Piddock Special Offer
Neil Rhodes Books
Well Cottage
Wern
Llanymynech
Shropshire
SY22 6PF

Please rush me a copy of Brian Piddock's extraordinary book! I enclose a cheque for £7.99p (made out to "*Neil Rhodes Books*"). This includes post & packaging!

Name

Address

Postcode

Telephone
number

email
address

Order extra copies of
"**How to write a how to write book**"
by Brian Piddock

The perfect present!
Give to all your friends and family!

Cut out and send to:
Brian Piddock Special Offer
Neil Rhodes Books
Well Cottage
Wern
Llanymynech
Shropshire
SY22 6PF

Please rush me a copy of Brian Piddock's extraordinary book! I enclose a cheque for £7.99p (made out to "*Neil Rhodes Books*"). This includes post & packaging!

Name

Address

Postcode

Telephone
number

email
address